# Maths Progress

## International 11–14

**Confidence • Fluency • Problem-solving • Progression**

**8**

**Workbook**

Pearson

Published by Pearson Education Limited, 80 Strand, London, WC2R 0RL.

www.pearsonschoolsandfecolleges.co.uk

Text © Pearson Education Limited 2020
Project managed and edited by Just Content Ltd
Typeset by PDQ Digital Media Solutions Ltd
Original illustrations © Pearson Education Limited 2020
Cover illustration by Robert Samuel Hanson

The rights of Greg Byrd, Keith Gallick, Sophie Goldie, Catherine Murphy, Amy O'Brien and Diane Oliver to be identified as authors of this work have been asserted by them in accordance with the Copyright, Designs and Patents Act 1988.

First published 2020

24

12

**British Library Cataloguing in Publication Data**
A catalogue record for this book is available from the British Library.

ISBN 978 1 292 32718 1

Printed in Great Britain by Bell and Bain Ltd, Glasgow

**Acknowledgements**
The publisher would like to thank Diane Oliver for her input and advice.

**Note from the publisher**
Pearson has robust editorial processes, including answer and fact checks, to ensure the accuracy of the content in this publication, and every effort is made to ensure this publication is free of errors. We are, however, only human, and occasionally errors do occur. Pearson is not liable for any misunderstandings that arise as a result of errors in this publication, but it is our priority to ensure that the content is accurate. If you spot an error, please do contact us at resourcescorrections@pearson.com so we can make sure it is corrected.

# Contents

# Welcome to Maths Progress International
## Workbooks

Starting a new course is exciting! We believe you will have fun with maths, while at the same time nurturing your confidence and raising your achievement. Here's how:

Start by **Mastering** fundamental knowledge and skills over a series of lessons.

**Guided questions** and partially worked solutions help you structure your answers.

Your teacher has online access to **Answers**.

A **confidence checker** at the end of every lesson helps you keep track of your strengths and weaknesses and suggests which questions from **Strengthen** you should try.

As well as hints that help you with specific questions, you'll find **Literacy hints** (to explain some unfamiliar terms) and **Strategy hints** (to help with working out).

**QR codes** give you direct access to worked example videos via your phone or tablet, providing plenty of support for tricky questions.

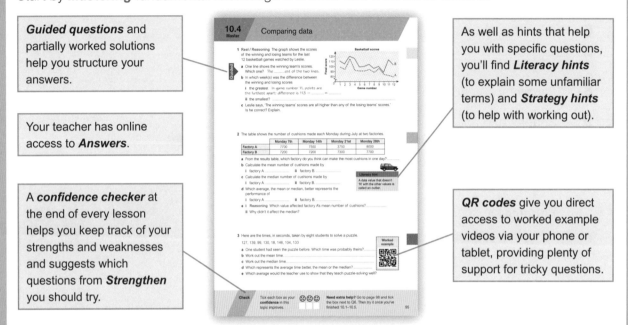

Choose only the topics in **Strengthen** that you need a bit more practice with. You'll find more hints here to lead you through specific questions

**Extend** helps you to apply the maths you know to some different situations.

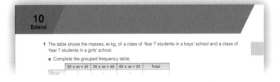

When you have finished the whole unit, a **Unit test** helps you see how much progress you are making. Keep track of your confidence and the questions you answered correctly in the Progression charts on pages 110–113.

**1** Work out

**a** $8 + -3 = 8 - 3 = $ ..............

**b** $9 - -4 = 9$ .............. $4 = $ ..............

Same signs (+ + or − −) are the same as +.
Different signs (+ − or − +) are the same as −.

**c** $5 - 8$ ..............................

**d** $-3 + 2$ ..............................

**e** $-4 - 4$ ..............................

**f** $-7 - -4$ ..............................

**g** $-5 + -3$ ..............................

**2** Work out the difference between each pair of numbers.

**a** 5 and 8 ..............................

**b** −5 and 8 ..............................

**c** 5 and −8 ..............................

**d** −5 and −8 ..............................

$8 - -5 = \square$

To find the difference between
two numbers, subtract the lower
one from the higher one.

**3** Work out

Multiplying same signs (+ × + or − × −)
gives +. Multiplying different signs
(+ × − or − × +) gives −.

**Worked
example**

**a** $-3 \times -5$ ..............................

**b** $5 \times -2$ ..............................

**c** $-8 \times 8$ ..............................

**d** $(-4) \times (-4)$ ..............................

**e** $10 \times (-2.2)$ ..............................

**f** $-2 \times -2 \times -2$ ..............................

**g** $3 \times -3 \times 3$ ..............................

**h** $-1 \times 1 \times -1$ ..............................

**4** Work out

**a** $-10 \div 2$ ..............................

**b** $12 \div -3$ ..............................

**c** $-25 \div 5$ ..............................

**d** $(-16) \div 4$ ..............................

**e** $30 \div (-10)$ ..............................

**f** $(-4) \div (-4)$ ..............................

**5** Expand the brackets to calculate these. Check your answer using the priority of operations.

**a** $4 \times (-2 + 5)$

$= 4 \times -2 + $ .......... $\times 5$

$= -8 + $ .......... $= $ ..............

Check: $4 \times (-2 + 5) = $ .......... $\times 3 = $ ..............

**b** $5 \times (-3 - 4)$

**6** Expand the brackets to calculate these. Check your answer using the priority of operations.

**a** $2 \times (-2 + 5) - 10$

**b** $-3(-2 + 6)$

**c** $-10(5 - 8)$

**d** $-2(-4 + 7) - 1$

**7** Work out

**a** $(-3)^2$ ..........

**b** $(-5)^2$ ..........

**c** $(-8)^2$ ..........

**Check**    Tick each box as your **confidence** in this topic improves.    ☹ 😐 ☺    **Need extra help?** Go to page 5 and tick the boxes next to Q1 and 2. Then try them once you've finished 1.1–1.4.

1

# Prime factor decomposition

**Guided**

**1 a** Draw a factor tree to find all the prime factors of 100.

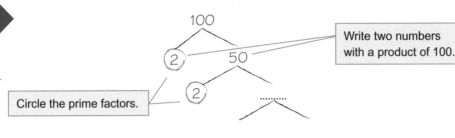

100

(2)  50

Write two numbers with a product of 100.

Circle the prime factors.

(2)

..........

..........    ..........

You can write a number as a product of prime number factors.
This is called prime factor decomposition.

**b** Write down the product of the prime factors.

$100 = 2 \times 2 \times$ ............... $\times$ ...............

> **Literacy hint**
>
> The product is the answer when you multiply two or more numbers.

**2** Write each number as a product of its prime factors.

**a** 60          **b** 84          **c** 250          **d** 360

**Guided**

**3** Find the HCF and LCM of 72 and 120.

$72 = 2^3 \times 3^2$

$120 = 2^3 \times 3 \times 5$

Write each number as a product of its prime factors.

You can use prime factor decomposition to find the HCF of two or more numbers.

Factors of 72          Factors of 120

3          $2^3$          5

3

Draw a Venn diagram. $3^2$ is a factor of 72 but not of 72 *and* 120.

HCF is $2^3 \times 3 =$ ...............

LCM is $2^3 \times 3 \times 3 \times 5 =$ ...............

Multiply the common prime factors together.

Multiply the common prime factors, the factors of only 72 and the factors of only 120 together.

**4** Use prime factor decomposition to find

**a** the HCF of 108 and 180          **b** the LCM of 30 and 55.

Draw Venn diagrams.

> **Worked example**
>
>

**Check** Tick each box as your **confidence** in this topic improves.

☹ 😐 ☺

**Need extra help?** Go to pages 5 and 6 and tick the boxes next to Q3–6. Then try them once you've finished 1.1–1.4.

**1 Reasoning** Sonia works out $4^2 \times 4^5$ like this:

$4 \times 4 \times 4 \times 4 \times 4 \times 4 \times 4 = 4^7$

How can you quickly find $4^2 \times 4^5$ without writing all the 4s?

> Look at the indices in the question and the answer.

> **Worked example**
>
>

**2** Write each product as a single power.

**a** $5^3 \times 5^4$ ...............

**b** $7^3 \times 7$ ...............

**c** $9^5 \times 9^3$ ...............

> When you multiply numbers written as powers of the same number, you add the indices. $7 = 7^1$.

> **Literacy hint**
>
> A single power means one number with a power. For example, $2^7$.

**3 Reasoning**

**a** Work out $\dfrac{3 \times 3 \times 3 \times 3 \times 3 \times 3}{3 \times 3 \times 3 \times 3}$ by cancelling. Write your answer as a power of 3. ...............

**b** Complete this: $3^6 \div 3^4 = 3^{\cdots}$

**c** How can you quickly find $3^6 \div 3^4$ without writing all the 3s?

> When you divide numbers written as powers of the same number, you subtract the indices.

**4** Write each of these as a single power.

**a** $8^7 \div 8^3$ ...............   **b** $5^8 \div 5^5$ ...............   **c** $4^6 \div 4$ ...............

> When you work out the power of a power, you multiply the indices.

**5** Write each of these as a single power.

**a** $(2^3)^2$ ...............   **b** $(10^2)^2$ ...............   **c** $(2^5)^2$ ...............

> A general rule is a rule that works for any numbers. Using letters shows that any number can be substituted.

**6 Reasoning** Complete these general rules for any number $a$.

**a** $a^m \times a^n = a^{\cdots + \cdots}$   **b** $a^m \div a^n = a^{\cdots - \cdots}$   **c** $(a^m)^n = a^{\cdots \times \cdots}$

**7 Reasoning**

**a** When you work out the answer to the divisions $\dfrac{3}{3}, \dfrac{10}{10}, \dfrac{15}{15}, \dfrac{60}{60}$ and $\dfrac{5^4}{5^4}$, what do you notice about dividing a number by itself?

**b** Complete this pattern: $\dfrac{5^4}{5^1} = 5^3, \dfrac{5^4}{5^2} = 5^{\cdots}, \dfrac{5^4}{5^3} = 5^{\cdots}, \dfrac{5^4}{5^4} = 5^{\cdots}$

**c** Complete this statement: 'Any number to the power of zero = ...............'

> Use your answers for $\frac{5^4}{5^4}$ in parts **a** and **b**.

**8** Write each calculation as a single power.

**a** $\dfrac{3^4 \times 3^5}{3^3}$ ...............   **b** $\dfrac{8^{10}}{8 \times 8^6}$ ...............   **c** $\dfrac{16 \times 32}{2^3 \times 2^4}$ ...............

> **Q8c Strategy hint**
>
> Start by writing each number as a power of 2.

---

**Check** | Tick each box as your **confidence** in this topic improves. |  | **Need extra help?** Go to page 6 and tick the boxes next to Q7–9. Then try them once you've finished 1.1–1.4.

**Guided**

**1** Work out

**a** $(5 + 7) \times 9 = 12 \times 9 = $ ...........

**b** $8 \times (5 - 3) = 8 \times $ .......... $= $ ..........

**c** $15 \times (12 - 2) = $ .......... $\times$ .......... $= $ ..........

**d** $18 \div (11 - 2) = 18 \div $ .......... $= $ ..........

**e** $(20 + 8) \div 2 = $ .......... $\div$ .......... $= $ ..........

Work out the calculation in the brackets first.

**2** Work from left to right to work out the answers.

**a** $3 \times 4 \div 2 = $ ...............

**b** $9 \div 3 \times 8 = $ ...............

**c** $18 + 7 - 5 = $ ...............

**d** $9 - 7 + 11 = $ ...............

Always work out the multiplication/division before the addition/subtraction.

**Guided**

**3** Work out

**a** $3 \times 7 + 5 = $ .......... $+ 5 = $ ..........

**b** $3 + 7 \times 5 = 3 + $ .......... $= $ ..........

**c** $40 \div 20 + 5 = $ .......... $+ 5 = $ ..........

**d** $40 + 20 \div 5 = 40 + $ .......... $= $ ..........

Work out the indices before multiplication/division and addition/subtraction.

**4** Work out

**a** $4^2 = $ ...............

**b** $4^2 + 8 = $ ..................... $= $ ...............

**c** $4^2 - 7 = $ ..................... $= $ ...............

**d** $4^2 \times 3 = $ ..................... $= $ ...............

**e** $4^2 \div 2 = $ ..................... $= $ ...............

**f** $2 \times 4^2 = $ ..................... $= $ ...............

**g** $7 + 4^2 = $ ..................... $= $ ...............

**h** $32 \div 4^2 = $ ..................... $= $ ...............

**5 a** $3 \times \sqrt{49} = $ ..................... $= $ ...............

**b** $3 + 4 \times \sqrt{49} = $ ..................... $= $ .................. $= $ ...............

**c** $\sqrt{49} \times 3 - 8 = $ ..................... $= $ ..................... $= $ ...............

**d** $2 + \sqrt{49} - 5 \times 2 = $ ..................... $= $ ..................... $= $ ..................... $= $ ...............

**6** Work out

**a** $(7 - 5)^4$ .....................

**b** $1000 - (5 - 2)^5$ .....................

Use the $x^y$ button on your calculator

**7** Work out

**a** $2^5 + 4 \times 5$ .....................

**b** $2 \times 4^4$ .....................

**c** $2^6 - \sqrt[3]{1331}$ .....................

**Check** Tick each box as your **confidence** in this topic improves.

**Need extra help?** Go to page 6 and tick the boxes next to Q10 and 11. Then try them once you've finished 1.1–1.4.

## Calculating with negative numbers

**1** Work out

Replace different signs with a minus (–). Replace same signs with a plus (+).

**a** 9 + −7 ..............................

**b** 7 − −9 ......................................

**c** −7 − −9 ..............................

**d** −9 + −7 .............................

**2** Work out

For multiplying and dividing: same signs give a positive answer; different signs give a negative answer.

**a** −5 × 9 ..............................

**b** −20 ÷ −4 ......................................

**c** −2 × −8 ..............................

**d** 16 ÷ −4 ......................................

## Prime factors

**3** Write each product using index notation (powers).

$7 \times 7 \times 7 = 7^3$

*Guided*

**a** $7 \times 7 \times 7 \times 5 \times 5 \times 5 \times 5 \times 2 = 7^3 \times 5^{\cdots} \times 2 =$ ................

Write the factors in numerical order: 2s, then 5s, then 7s.

**b** $3 \times 11 \times 11 \times 11 \times 11 \times 11 \times 13 \times 13$ ................

**c** $2 \times 2 \times 2 \times 2 \times 5 \times 5 \times 5 \times 7 \times 7 \times 11$ ................

**4 a** Draw a factor tree for each number until you end up with just prime factors.

**b** Use index notation to write each number as the product of its prime factors.

**i**

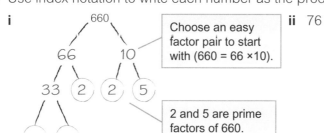

Choose an easy factor pair to start with (660 = 66 ×10).

2 and 5 are prime factors of 660.

**ii** 76          **iii** 468

$660 = 2^{\cdots} \times$ .......... $\times 5 \times$ ................

**5** This is how James works out the HCF of 18 and 60.

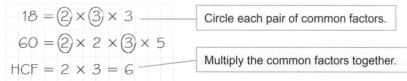

Circle each pair of common factors.

Multiply the common factors together.

Work out the HCF of each pair of numbers.

**a** 32 and 40

**b** 45 and 75

First work out the prime factor decomposition.

☐ **6** This is how Sam works out the LCM of 18 and 60.

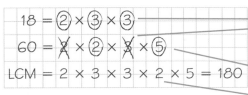

> Circle one factor at a time from the first number. If it appears in the second number, cross it off.

> Circle any factors that are not crossed off from the second number.

> Multiply all the circled factors together.

> First find the prime factor decomposition.

Work out the LCM of each pair of numbers.

**a** 20 and 32          **b** 45 and 60

## Indices and priority of operations

☐ **7** Write each calculation as a single power.

**Guided**

**a** $2^3 \times 2^4 = 2^{..... + .....} = 2^{.....}$

**b** $5^4 \times 5^6 = 5^{..... + .....} = 5^{.....}$

**c** $6^3 \times 6$ ......................

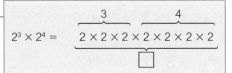

$$2^3 \times 2^4 = \underbrace{\overbrace{2 \times 2 \times 2}^{3} \times \overbrace{2 \times 2 \times 2 \times 2}^{4}}_{\square}$$

> **Worked example**

☐ **8** Write each calculation as a single power.

**Guided**

**a** $3^5 \div 3^2 = 3^{..... - .....} = 3^{.....}$

**b** $4^9 \div 4^6$ ......................

**c** $10^{12} \div 10^7$ ......................

$$3^5 \div 3^2 = \frac{\overbrace{\cancel{3} \times \cancel{3} \times 3 \times 3 \times 3}^{5}}{\underbrace{\cancel{3} \times \cancel{3}}_{2}}$$

☐ **9** Write each calculation as a single power.

**Guided**

**a** $(5^3)^2 = 5^3 \times 5^3 = 5^{.....}$          **b** $(3^2)^4 = 3^2 \times 3^2 \times ....... \times ....... = 3^{.....}$

**c** $(7^3)^5$ ......................

☐ **10** Work out

**a** $(-2)^2$ ......................          **b** $13 + (-2)^2$ ......................          **c** $13 - (-2)^2$ ......................

negative × negative =

☐ **11** Copy and complete.

| | | |
|---|---|---|
| **a**   $2 \times 5 + 6$ $= ....... + 6$ $= .......$ | **b**   $7 - 3 \times 2$ $= 7 - .......$ $= .......$ | **c**   $4^2 - 11$ $= .... - 11$ $= .......$ |
| **d**   $27 \div 3^2$ $= 27 \div .......$ $= .......$ | **e**   $(4 + 5) \times 7$ $= ......... \times 7$ $= .......$ | **f**   $(-5)^2 - (9 + 7)$ $= ....... - (9 + 7)$ $= ....... - .......$ $= .......$ |

Do multiplication/division before addition/subtraction. Do indices before multiplication/division and addition/subtraction. Do brackets before indices, multiplication/division and addition/subtraction.

1 **Real** Glenville recorded the temperature every four hours during one day.
$-1.2\,°C$, $-3.7\,°C$, $-3.8\,°C$, $4.3\,°C$, $6.1\,°C$, $2.2\,°C$

   a Find the median temperature.

   b Estimate the mean temperature.

   c Work out the range.

2 **Problem-solving / Reasoning** Here is the prime factor decomposition of a number.

   .......... $= 2 \times 3^2 \times$ ..........

   Start by working out $2 \times 3^2$

   The number is less than 100.
   What is the number? Explain how you made your decision.

3 **Reasoning** The area of a square is $3^8$ cm$^2$.
What is the length of one side?
Write your answer as a power of 3.

$3^8$ cm$^2$

Write each number as the product
of its prime factors.

4 a Find the highest common factor of 18, 36 and 60.

   $18 = ②\times③\times 3$, $36 = ②\times 2 \times③\times 3$, $60 = 2 \times 2 \times$ ....... $\times$ ......., HCF = .......

   b Find the lowest common multiple of 6, 10 and 14.

   $6 = 2 \times 3$, $10 = 2 \times$ ......., $14 =$ ....... $\times$ ......., LCM = ........................................

   c Joe has written two numbers as products of their prime factors: $2^5 \times 3^3$ and $2^4 \times 3^4$.
   Work out the highest common factor and lowest common multiple of the two numbers.

5 Work these out. Check your answers using a calculator.

   a $\dfrac{3 + 3^3}{\sqrt{25} + 1}$ .............................................

   b $\sqrt[3]{7^2 + 15}$ ...........................................................

   c $\dfrac{5^2 + 8}{\sqrt{5^3 - 4}}$ .............................................

   d $\dfrac{2^3 + 2^2 + 2}{\sqrt[3]{2^2 + 2^2}}$ .............................................

6 a Work out the prime factor decomposition of these numbers.

   i   160     ii     180     iii     240

   b What is the HCF of 160, 180 and 240? .....................

   c What is the LCM of 160, 180 and 240? .....................

Guided Guided Guided

**7** Write each of these as a product of primes.

**a** $15^3 \times 3^2 \times 5^4$ ................................................................................

**b** $2^4 \times 14^3 \times 7^2$ ................................................................................

**c** $10^3 \times 12^2 \times 25^3$ ................................................................................

First write $15^3$ as $(3 \times 5)^3$.

**8** Evaluate these. Give each answer as a fraction in its simplest form.

**a** $\dfrac{10 \times 5^{12}}{5^{15}}$
           **b** $\dfrac{15 \times 3^4}{3^6}$
           **c** $\dfrac{20 \times 5^{14}}{5^7 \times 5^9} = \dfrac{20}{5^2} = \dfrac{\square \times \square}{5^2} = \dfrac{2}{\square} = \dfrac{\square}{\square}$

**9** Use the formula $s = ut + \frac{1}{2}at^2$ to work out the value of $s$ when

**a** $a = 4$, $t = 3$ and $u = 5$

**b** $a = 6$, $t = -5$ and $u = 2$

**10 Problem-solving** In these multiplication pyramids,
the number in a brick is the product of the two bricks below it.
Work out the missing entries. Write each answer in index form.

**a**
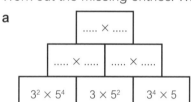

$3^2 \times 5^4 \times 3 \times 5^2 = 3^3 \times 5^6$

**b**
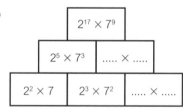

$2^5 \times 7^3 \times 2^{\square} \times 7^{\square} = 2^{17} \times 7^9$

**11 Reasoning** Use your answers from Q10 to help you complete these general rules.

**a** $a^p \times b^q \times a^r \times b^s = a^{\,\cdots\cdots} \times b^{\,\cdots\cdots}$
        **b** $\dfrac{a^p \times b^q}{a^r \times b^s} = a^{\,\cdots\cdots} \times b^{\,\cdots\cdots}$

**1** The recommended temperature of a domestic refrigerator is 4°C.
The recommended temperature of a domestic freezer is −18°C.

   **a** Work out the difference in temperature. ................................................................

   **b** An industrial freezer should be 4°C colder than a domestic freezer.
      What is the temperature of an industrial freezer? ................................................................

**2** Write each of these numbers as a product of prime factors.

   **a** 140                              **b** 504

**3** Write each calculation as a single power.

   **a** $7^2 \times 7^6$ ...............................   **b** $5^8 \times 5 \times 5^3$ ...............................

   **c** $10^9 \div 10^5$ ...............................   **d** $(3^5)^4$ ...............................

**4** Use your answers to Q2 to work out

   **a** the HCF of 140 and 504 ...............................

   **b** the LCM of 140 and 504. ...............................

**5** Work out

   **a** $7 + 3 \times 2$ ...............................   **b** $\sqrt{16}$ ...............................

   **c** $2^3$ ...............................   **d** $5 \times 3^2$ ...............................

   **e** $\sqrt{9^2 + 19}$ ...............................   **f** $\sqrt[3]{27}$ ...............................

**6** Work out

   **a** $10 - {-3}$ ...............................   **b** $5 \times {-3}$ ...............................

   **c** $-20 \div -2$ ...............................   **d** $(-5)^2$ ...............................

   **e** $2^2 \times 5^2$ ...............................   **f** $10 - (\sqrt[3]{8} \times \sqrt{25})$ ...............................

**7** Match each white card to the correct shaded card.

   **A** $(a^m)^n$    **B** $a^m \div a^n$    **C** $a^m \times a^n$    **D** $a^{m+n}$    **E** $a^{mn}$    **F** $a^{m-n}$

**1** Use the **inverse function** to find each missing **input**.

**a**

□ → [ × 3 ) → 21

□ ← ( ) ← 21

**b**

□ → [ − 5 ) → 12

□ ← ( ) ← 12

A **function** is a rule. The function +3 adds 3 to a number. The **inverse function** is −3 because it reverses the effect of the function +3.

2 → [ + 3 ) → 5

2 ← ( − 3 ) ← 5

**2** Complete the function machines to solve these **equations**.

**a** $x - 5 = 3$

$x$ → [ − 5 ) → 3

□ ← ( ) ← 3

$x = □$

**b** $2x = 12$

$x$ → [ × 2 ) → 12

□ ← ( ) ← 12

$x = □$

An **equation** contains an unknown number (a letter) and an '=' sign. To solve an equation means to work out the unknown number.

**3** Solve these equations.

**a** $\dfrac{t}{4} = 8$

$\dfrac{4 \times t}{4} = 4 \times 8$

$t =$

Check: .............. ÷ 4 = 8 ✓

**b** $x + 5 = 19$

Balance the equation by multiplying both sides by 4.

Check by replacing $t$ in the equation with your solution.

Visualise the function machines to decide which inverse to use.

$t$ → [ ÷ 4 ) → 8

□ ← ( × 4 ) ← 8

In an equation, the expressions on both sides of the equals sign have the same value. You can visualise them on balanced scales.

| $t + 3$ | = | 8 |

To stay balanced, do the same operation to both sides.

| $t + 3 - 3$ | = | $8 - 3$ |

This is called the **balancing method**.

**4 a** Write an equation for these six angles.

..................................

**b** Solve your equation to find the value of $t$.

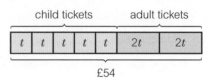

What do the angles on a straight line add up to?

**5** **Problem-solving / Modelling** Tickets for 2 adults and 5 children to a football match come to £54. An adult ticket costs twice as much as a child ticket. Work out the price of an adult ticket.

Use $t$ to stand for the cost of a child ticket.

child tickets       adult tickets

| $t$ | $t$ | $t$ | $t$ | $t$ | $2t$ | $2t$ |

£54

**Check** Tick each box as your **confidence** in this topic improves.

**Need extra help?** Go to page 14 and tick the boxes next to Q1–3. Then try them once you've finished 2.1–2.4.

10

**Guided**

**1** Draw function machines to solve each equation.

**a** $3x + 2 = 14$          **b** $5p - 1 = 34$          **c** $\dfrac{d}{3} + 10 = 12$

$x \rightarrow \boxed{\times 3} \rightarrow \boxed{+ 2} \rightarrow 14$

$\square \leftarrow \boxed{\square} \leftarrow \boxed{- 2} \leftarrow 14$

$x = \square$

**Guided**

**2** Use the balancing method to solve these equations.

**a** $3x + 5 = 17$

$3x + 5 - 5 = 17 - 5$

$\quad\quad 3x = 12$

$\quad\quad\quad x = \text{.......}$

Balance the equation by subtracting 5 from each side.

Balance again by dividing both sides by 3.

**b** $2x - 5 = 11$

Check: $3 \times \text{...............} + 5 = 17$ ✓

**3 STEM** Substitute the values given into each formula.
Then solve the equation to find the unknown value.

**a** $y = mx + c$
Find $x$ when $y = 17$, $m = 3$ and $c = -4$.

**b** $s = ut + \dfrac{1}{2}at^2$
Work out $a$ when $s = 30$, $u = 4$ and $t = 3$.

**4** Solve the equation $-2x + 9 = -3$.

**5 Modelling** Koa says, 'I think of a number, multiply it by 4 and add 5.
My answer is 49.'

**a** Write an equation to show Koa's calculation. Use $n$ for the number he thinks of.

**b** Solve your equation to work out Koa's number.

**Worked example**

**6 Modelling** Work out the sizes of the angles.

**a**

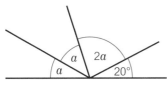

**b**

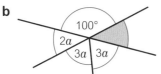

Work out the value of the letter first.

What do you know about the shaded angle?

**Check**   Tick each box as your **confidence** in this topic improves.   ☹ 😐 😊

**Need extra help?** Go to page 14 and tick the boxes next to Q4 and 5. Then try them once you've finished 2.1–2.4.

11

**1** Solve these equations.

**a** $4x - 1 = 3x + 2$

> You need to end up with $x = \square$, so start by subtracting $3x$ from both sides, which leaves an $x$ term on the left-hand side and no $x$ term on the right.

**b** $8x - 3 = 7x - 1$

$4x - 3x - 1 = 3x - 3x + 2$

$x - 1 = 2$

> Simplify.

$x - 1 + 1 = 2 + 1$

> Add 1 to both sides.

$x = \text{.........}$

Check: $4 \times \text{.........} - 1 = \text{.........}$

$3 \times \text{.........} + 2 = \text{.........}$

> Substitute $x = \square$ into both sides to check they have the same value.

**c** $6t - 4 = 4t + 4$

**d** $6x = 3(x + 2)$

**e** $8(x - 6) = 2(x + 6)$ — Expand the brackets first.

**2 Modelling** Deepak says, 'I think of a number, multiply it by 10 and subtract 6. When I start again with the same number, double it and add 12, I get the same answer.'

**a** Write an expression for each of Deepak's calculations. ............................ and ...........................

**b** Write an equation to show that both calculations give the same answer. ........................................

**c** Solve your equation to find the number Deepak was thinking of.

**3** Solve these equations.

**a** $2x + 5 = 4x - 1$

**b** $5y + 4 = 2(y + 5)$

**c** $6(z + 8) = 8(z + 5)$

**4 Problem-solving / Reasoning** Write an equation and solve it to find the size of each angle.

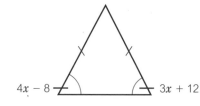

What do you know about the two angles?

$4x - 8$  $3x + 12$

**Check** Tick each box as your **confidence** in this topic improves.

☹ 😐 ☺

**Need extra help?** Go to page 14 and tick the boxes next to Q7. Then try them once you've finished 2.1–2.4.

12

**1** $a - b = 5$

   **a** If $a = 7$ what is the value of $b$? ..............

   $a$ and $b$ are both positive integers. $a$ is smaller than 10.

   **b** List all the possible values of $a$ and $b$.

> A systematic approach will ensure you list all the possible values.
> e.g.    $a = 9$, $b = $ ...
>       $a = 8$, $b = $ ....

**2 Problem-solving** $2x + y = $ a multiple of 5.

   **a** Find three possible values of $x$ and $y$.

..................................................................................

   **b** What do you notice about your values of $x$ and $y$?

..................................................................................................................

**3 Real / Reasoning** Write a formula for converting

   **a** minutes ($m$) into seconds ($s$) ..............

   **b** seconds ($s$) into minutes ($m$) ..............

   **c** hours ($h$) into minutes ($m$) ..............

   **d** minutes ($m$) into hours ($h$). ..............

**4** Here is a regular hexagon. The length of one of the sides is $x$.

   **a** Write down a formula for calculating the perimeter, $P$.

   **b** Use the formula to calculate the perimeter when

     **i** $x = 11$         **ii** $x = 0.7$

   **c** Work out the value of $x$ when

     **i** $P = 24$         **ii** $P = 15$

**5 Real / Problem-solving** A cleaner works out how long (in hours) it will take him to clean a house by multiplying the number of rooms by 0.5 and adding 1.

   **a** How long will it take him to clean a house with 5 rooms? ........................

   **b** Write a formula that connects the number of rooms in a house ($r$) with the number of hours it will take to clean it ($T$). ........................

   **c** If a house takes 8 hours to clean, how many rooms does it have? ........................

## Solving equations

Use number facts and times tables.

**1** Work out the value of each symbol.

   **a** $5 + \Diamond = 9$ ...............

   **b** $3 \times \square = 15$ ...............

   **c** $\dfrac{\nabla}{4} = 2$ ...............

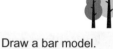

**2** Solve these equations. Check each answer.

   **a** $p + 4 = 17$        **b** $21 = 12 + q$        **c** $r - 8 = 10$

Draw a bar model.
$p + 4$

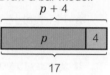

**3** Solve these equations. Check each answer.

   **a** $4d = 20$        **b** $3e = -21$        **c** $\dfrac{f}{10} = 22$

Draw a bar model.
$4d$

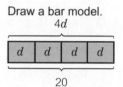

**4** Solve these equations.

   **a** $5x - 3 = 7$   | Add 3 to both sides. |

      $5x = 10$

          | Divide both sides by $\square$. |

      $x = $ ...............

   **b** $3y + 4 = 16$

   **c** $\dfrac{z}{2} + 3 = 7$

**Worked example**

**5** Solve these equations.

   **a** $20 - 2x = 8$        **b** $12 - 4x = 4$

      $20 = 2x + 8$   | Subtract 8 from both sides. |

      ....... $= 2x$

      $x = $ .......

   **c** $5 - 3x = 11$

## More complex equations and working with formulae

**6** Use the formula $W = ax - d$ to find the value of $a$ when $W = 3$, $x = 7$ and $d = 11$.

Substitute in the numbers you know, then solve to work out the value of $a$.

**7** Solve

   **a** $5(x - 2) = 3(x + 2)$        **b** $4(x + 3) = 6(x + 1)$

      $5x - 10 = 3x + 6$   | Expand the brackets. |

      ....... $- 10 = 6$   | Subtract $3x$ from both sides. |

      ............... $= $ ...............

         $x = $ ...............

**8 Modelling**

   **a** Write an equation for these angles. ...............

   **b** Solve to find $n$.

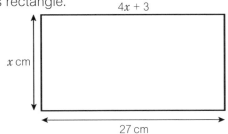

   **c** Write down the size of the largest angle. ..............

**9** Work out the lengths of the sides of this rectangle.

$4x + 3$

$x$ cm

27 cm

> **Strategy hint**
>
> Write an equation. Find $x$, then use this value to find the length of each side.

**10 a i** 1 metre = ............... cm

     **ii** 5 metres = ............... cm

     **iii** 12 metres = ............... cm

   **b** Complete.
     Length in cm = length in m × ...............

   **c** Which of these formulae converts between length in metres ($m$) and length in cm ($c$)?

     $m = 100c$      $m = \dfrac{c}{100}$     $c = 100m$     $c = \dfrac{100}{m}$

**11 Problem solving**   Parth puts three sugar flowers on the top of each cupcake he makes.
He knows that he breaks 4 flowers each time he bakes.
Write down how many flowers he should buy to make

   **a** 2 cupcakes ...............

   **b** 5 cupcakes. ...............

   **c** Which of these formulae should he use to work out the number of sugar flowers ($s$) he should
buy for $c$ cupcakes?

     $s = 3c + 4$     $s = 3(c + 4)$     $s = 4c + 3$     $s = 7c$

1 Use the formula $S = 180(n - 2)$ to work out $n$ when $S = 720$.

2 **Modelling / Problem-solving** The length of a rectangle is twice its width.

   a Sketch the rectangle.
   Label its width $w$.
   Write an **expression** for the length of the rectangle in terms of $w$.

   > **Literacy hint**
   >
   > An **expression** in terms of $w$ includes the letter $w$.

   b The perimeter of the rectangle is 30 cm.
   Work out the length and the width.

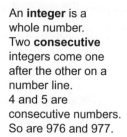

3 **Modelling / Problem-solving** Two consecutive integers add to make 165.
   What are these two numbers?

   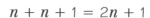

   First number $= n$, second number $= n + 1$

   $n + n + 1 = 2n + 1$

   $2n + 1 = 165$

   > Write an expression for each of the two integers. Then add your expressions together.

   > The two integers add to make 165. Write this as an equation.

   Solve your equation to find the value of $n$ (the first number).
   Write down the two integers.

   An **integer** is a whole number.
   Two **consecutive** integers come one after the other on a number line.
   4 and 5 are consecutive numbers. So are 976 and 977.

4 **Modelling / Problem-solving** The sum of three consecutive integers is 78.
   What are the three integers?

   Three **consecutive** integers come one after the other on a number line.
   Three consecutive integers: $n$, $n + 1$, $n + 2$.

**5 Real / Modelling** Madison and Mason are twins. They have a cat called Humpty.
The twins are $t$ years old and are 11 years older than Humpty.

   **a** The total age of all three is 34.
     Write an expression for their total age. ................

   **b** Write an equation and solve it to find $t$.

   **c** How old is Humpty? ...............

Humpty's age is $t - 11$.

**6 Modelling** Audrey is 4 years younger than her husband.
Their total age is 154.
What are their ages?

**7** The sum of two numbers is 18. Their difference is 4.
What are the two numbers?

Write two equations to represent the information you have been given.
e.g.    $x + y = ...$
        $x = y - ....$

**8** I think of a number. 3 less than 4 times my number is equal to 1 more than 2 times my number.
What is the number I thought of?

**9** $a = \dfrac{1}{b} + 4$ and $b \geqslant 2$.
What is the largest value that $a$ could have?

Try different values of $b$.

1 Solve these equations.

   **a** $x - 5 = 2$                  **b** $3x = 27$                **c** $\dfrac{x}{4} = 8$

2 Solve these equations.

   **a** $2x + 4 = 10$            **b** $\dfrac{x}{4} - 3 = 2$          **c** $2(x + 3) = 22$

3 Work out the size of each angle in this triangle.

4 Use the formula $A = \dfrac{1}{2}bh + 2h^2$ to work out the value of $b$ when $h = 10$ and $A = 410$.

5 Solve the equation $4(x + 1) = 2(x + 3)$.

6 These two rectangles have the same area.
  Work out the value of $x$.

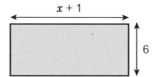
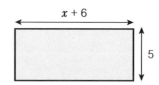

7 $2x - y = 7$
  If $x$ and $y$ are both positive integers, give three possible pairs of values for $x$ and $y$.

8 Write a formula for converting someone's age in years ($y$) into their age in months ($m$).

**1** Write an expression for each perimeter. Write your answer in its simplest form.

**a**

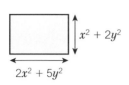

$x^2 + 2y^2$

$2x^2 + 5y^2$

**b**

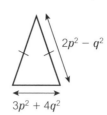

$2p^2 - q^2$

$3p^2 + 4q^2$

**2 a** Add together any two of the expressions linked by lines.

**b** Repeat part **a** in as many different ways as you can.

**c** Add all three expressions together.

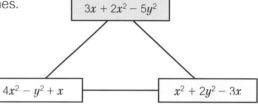

$3x + 2x^2 - 5y^2$

$4x^2 - y^2 + x$         $x^2 + 2y^2 - 3x$

**3** Expand and simplify

> Expand the brackets. Multiply terms in the second bracket by –2.

**Guided**

**a** $5(x + 3) + 2(x - 7)$

$= 5x + \text{.......} + 2x - \text{.......}$ — Expand the brackets.

$= 7x + \text{..........}$ — Collect like terms.

**b** $3(a + 2) - 2(a + 5)$

$= 3a + \text{.......} - 2a - \text{.......}$

$= a - \text{..........}$          Collect like terms.

**c** $3(y - 3) + 2(y + 5)$          **d** $5(c + 1) - 2(c - 3)$          **e** $4(h - 1) - 3(h + 2)$

**4 a** Write an expression for the area of the larger rectangle.

**b** Write an expression for the area of the smaller rectangle.

**c** Write an expression for the shaded area.

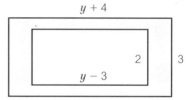

$y + 4$

$y - 3$

2          3

**5 Reasoning** The = and ≡ signs are missing from these statements. Write the correct sign for each one to show whether it is an equation or an identity.

> An equation has an equals (=) sign. It is true for particular values.
> For example, $3x + 2 = 14$ is only true for $x = 4$.
> The identity symbol (≡) shows that two expressions are always equivalent.
> For example, $x + 2x + 4 \equiv 3x + 4$.

**a** $3x + 2x \text{..........} 5x$          **b** $2x + 3 \text{..........} 5$

**c** $3 \times a \times a \times a \text{..........} 3a^3$          **d** $4p^2 \text{..........} 4p \times 2$

**e** $7d - 3 \text{..........} 4d + 3d - 2 - 1$          **f** $2 \times r \times r + 3 \times r \text{..........} 2r^2 + 3r$

**6 a Reasoning** Show that $2^3 + 2^3 \equiv 2^4$.          Work out the value of both sides.

**b** Is $x^3 + x^3 \equiv x^4$ true for all values of $x$? Explain your answer.

---

**Check**          Tick each box as your **confidence** in this topic improves.          ☹ 😐 ☺          **Need extra help?** Go to page 24 and tick the box next to Q1. Then try it once you've finished 3.1–3.5.

**1 Reasoning**

**a** Simplify

    **i** $3^2 \times 3^5$ ..........................    **ii** $5^2 \times 5^5$ ..........................    **iii** $x^2 \times x^5$ ..........................

**b** Write a rule to explain what you do to indices when you multiply powers of the same **variable**.

A **variable** is a letter that represents a number.

**c** Complete

    **i** $4^7 \div 4^5 = \dfrac{4^7}{4^5} = \dfrac{4 \times 4 \times 4 \times 4 \times 4 \times 4 \times 4}{4 \times 4 \times 4 \times 4 \times 4} = 4^{\cdots}$

    **ii** $x^7 \div x^5 = \dfrac{x^7}{x^5} = \dfrac{x \times x \times x \times x \times x \times x \times x}{x \times x \times x \times x \times x} = x^{\cdots}$

**d** Write a rule to explain what you do to indices when you divide powers of the same variable.

**e** Simplify  **i** $(3^2)^5$ ..........................   **ii** $(4^2)^5$ ..........................   **iii** $(x^2)^5$ ..........................

**f** Write a rule to explain what you do to indices when you raise a power of a variable to another power, as in Q1**e iii.**

$$p^4 \times p^7 = p^{4+7} = p^{\square}$$

**2 Simplify**

  **a** $p^4 \times p^7$ ..............................   **b** $r^{14} \div r^8$ ..............................   **c** $(e^4)^5$ ..............................

**3 Simplify**

**a** $\dfrac{20x^5}{4x^2}$    $\boxed{\dfrac{20}{4} = 5 \text{ and } \dfrac{x^5}{x^2} = x^3}$    **b** $\dfrac{5y^4 \times 12y^2}{4y^5}$    $\boxed{\dfrac{12}{4} = 3 \text{ and } \dfrac{y^4 \times y^2}{y^5} = y^{\square}}$

$= 5x^{\cdots}$            $= \dfrac{5y^4 \times \overset{3}{\cancel{12}}y^2}{\cancel{4}y^5} = 15$ ..............

**c** $\dfrac{18a^7}{6a^5}$ ..............................   **d** $\dfrac{15t^8}{3t^3}$ ..............................   **e** $\dfrac{3p^3 \times 10p^7}{5p^8}$ ..............................

**4 Problem-solving** This is part of Sarah's classwork. Her pen has leaked ink onto her page.

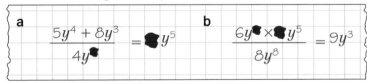

**a** $\dfrac{5y^4 + 8y^3}{4y^\blacksquare} = \blacksquare y^5$     **b** $\dfrac{6y^\blacksquare \times \blacksquare y^5}{8y^8} = 9y^3$

Rewrite Sarah's answers in full.

**a**                   **b**

**Worked example**

**5 Simplify**

  **a** $(5y^2)^2$ ..............   **b** $(2y^2)^3$ ..............   **c** $(4y^5)^2$ ..............

**Check**    Tick each box as your **confidence** in this topic improves.    ☹ 😐 ☺    **Need extra help?** Go to pages 24 and 25 and tick the boxes next to Q3–7. Then try them once you've finished 3.1–3.5.

**Guided**

**1** Write down the common factors of

  **a** 6 and $4p$                        **b** $6x$ and 10

  Factors of 6: 1, 2, 3, 6

  Factors of $4p$: 1, 2, 4, $p$, $2p$, $4p$

  Common factors of 6 and $4p$: 1, 2

  **c** 9 and $12t$

Expanding removes brackets from an expression. **Factorising** inserts brackets into an expression.

expand

$$6(a + 3) \;=\; 6a + 18$$

factorise

**2** Write down the HCF of

  **a** $6t$ and 12 ..............................

  **b** 14 and $21x$ ..............................

To factorise $6a + 18$, write the common factor of its terms, 6, outside the brackets. This is called 'taking out the common factor'.

**Guided**

**3** Complete these factorisations.

  **a** $5x + 15 = 5( \ldots\ldots + 3)$

> 5 is a common factor of both $5x$ and 15.
> Write 5 in front of the bracket. Divide both terms by 5 to work out the values in the bracket.

  **b** $14x + 7 = 7( \ldots\ldots + \ldots\ldots )$

  **c** $6x - 9 = 3( \ldots\ldots - \ldots\ldots )$    **d** $10x - 15 = 5( \ldots\ldots - \ldots\ldots )$    **e** $18x + 6 = \ldots\ldots (3x + \ldots\ldots)$

  **f** $25x - 5 = \ldots\ldots (5x - \ldots\ldots)$    **g** $4x + 12$ ..............................    **h** $27 - 9x$ ..............................

**4** Factorise each expression.

  **a** $5x + 20$ ..........................    **b** $3x - 12$ ..........................

  **c** $20x - 10$ ..........................    **d** $5x - 25$ ..........................

  **e** $12 + 6x$ ..........................    **f** $9 - 36x$ ..........................

Check your factorisation by expanding the brackets.

**Worked example**

**5** In how many different ways can the expression $6x + 12$ be factorised?

To factorise completely, write the highest common factor outside the brackets.

**6** Factorise completely.

  **a** $4x + 6$ ..........................    **b** $9t + 12$ ..........................

  **c** $16g + 32$ ..........................    **d** $20d - 5$ ..........................

  **e** $8 - 4w$ ..........................    **f** $8 + 18x$ ..........................

  **g** $120q + 40$ ..........................    **h** $44 + 22y$ ..........................

**7** Factorise completely.

  **a** $6a + 2b + 8$ ..........................

  **b** $20 + 30p + 15q$ ..........................

  **c** $ab + 3a + 9a$ ..........................

$2(\square + \square + \square)$

**Check**    Tick each box as your **confidence** in this topic improves.    ☹ 😐 ☺    **Need extra help?** Go to page 25 and tick the boxes next to Q8–9. Then try them once you've finished 3.1–3.5.

**Guided**

**1** Expand

  **a** $x(x^2 + 3x) = x^3 + $ .........................................

  **b** $2y^3(5y^2 - 3y)$ .........................................

  **c** $3x(4x^2 + 2x + 5)$ .........................................

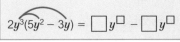

$$2y^3(5y^2 - 3y) = \boxed{\phantom{0}}y^{\square} - \boxed{\phantom{0}}y^{\square}$$

**2** Expand and simplify

  **a** $3(x + 2y) + 2(2x + y)$        **b** $2a(a^2 - 5) + 4a(3 + a^2)$

First expand the two brackets.
Then collect like terms.

**3** Write the highest common factor of each pair.

  **a** $y^3$ and $y^4$ ...............

  **b** $a^3$ and $a$ ...............

  **c** $12x^5$ and $8x^3$ ...............

  **d** $ab^2$ and $a^2b$ ...............

$y^3 = \textcircled{y} \times \textcircled{y} \times \textcircled{y}$
$y^4 = \textcircled{y} \times \textcircled{y} \times \textcircled{y} \times y$

**4** Factorise

**Guided**

  **a** $12x^2 + 8x$ — | The HCF of $12x^2$ and $8x$ is $4x$. |

    $4x(3x + 2)$

    | $4x \times 3x = 12x^2$ and $4x \times 2 = 8x$ |

    Check:

    $4x(3x + 2) = 12x^2 + 8x$

  **b** $25x^3 - 10x$

  **c** $21x - 14x^2$     **d** $24y + 18y^2$     **e** $20y^5 + 12y^3$

To factorise an expression
completely, take out the
highest common factor
(HCF) of its terms.

**Worked
example**

**5** **Problem-solving / Reasoning**

  **a** Show that each of these statements is an identity.

    **i** $2x^3 + 4x^2(x + 1) \equiv 2x^2(3x + 2)$

Expand the left-hand side and
rewrite it as the right-hand side.

    **ii** $5y(y^2 + 2y) - 2y(y^2 + 2y) \equiv 2y^2(y + 3) + y^3$

  **b** Work out the missing numbers in this identity.

    ....... $p(p^3 - 2) - p(2p^3 - .......) \equiv p(p^3 - 2) + 3p$

**Check** | Tick each box as your **confidence** in this topic improves. | ☹ ☺ ☻ □ □ □ | **Need extra help?** Go to pages 25 and 26 and tick the boxes next to Q10–12. Then try them once you've finished 3.1–3.5.

22

**Guided**

**1** Find the value of these **linear expressions** when $p = 5$, $q = 7$ and $r = -2$.

  **a** $2q + 5r$

    $= 2 \times 7 + 5 \times -2$

    $= \ldots\ldots\ldots$

> A **linear expression** is one where the highest power is 1. For example, $3x + 2$ and $2p - q$ are linear expressions. $3x^2 + 2$ is not a linear expression.

  **b** $3(p + 6) + q + r$         **c** $4(q - r) - 6p$

**2** Substitute $m = 2$, $n = 3$ and $p = -5$ into

  **a** $m(3m + 4n)$        **b** $n^2(m + p^2)$        **c** $3m(8 + n) + n^2$

**3** Solve

**Guided**

  **a** $5(p + 7) = 23 + 2(4p + 3)$

    $5p + 35 = 23 + 8p + 6$

    $5p + 35 = 8p + 29$

    $35 - \ldots\ldots = 8p - \ldots\ldots$

    $\ldots\ldots = \ldots\ldots\, p$

        $p = \ldots\ldots\ldots$

> Multiply out the brackets.

> Collect like terms on the right-hand side: $23 + 6 = 29$

> Rearrange to get like terms on both sides.

> Simplify and then solve.

**Worked example**

  **b** $6(2q - 3) = 26 - 4(q - 9)$       **c** $3(5m - 4) = 6m + 7 - 4(1 - m)$

**4 Problem-solving** In this diagram the shaded shapes have the same area.

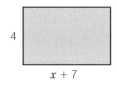

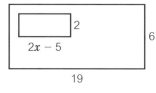

Write an expression for the area of each shape.

Work out the value of $x$.

**5 Problem-solving** A photograph is printed in the centre of a piece of paper measuring 7 cm by $(x + 8)$ cm. The photograph measures 5 cm by $(x + 6)$ cm. The area of the border around the photograph is 50 cm².

**Strategy hint**

Draw a diagram.

  **a** Work out the value of $x$.

  **b** Work out the dimensions of the paper and of the photograph.

## Simplifying and substituting into expressions

**1** Complete

How many $x^2$ are there altogether?

   **a** $4x^2 + 3x^2 = \ldots\ldots x^2$

   **b** $5p^2 - 2p^2 = \ldots\ldots\ldots$

   **c** $2y^2 + 7y^2 - 4y^2 = \ldots\ldots\ldots$

**2** Find the value of each expression when $x = -3$ and $y = 5$.

**Guided**

   **a** $x + y^2$

   $= \ldots\ldots\ldots + 5^2$

   $= \ldots\ldots\ldots + \ldots\ldots\ldots$

   $= \ldots\ldots\ldots$

   **b** $2x^2 - y$

   $= 2 \times (\ldots\ldots)^2 - \ldots\ldots\ldots$

   $= \ldots\ldots\ldots - \ldots\ldots\ldots$

   $= \ldots\ldots\ldots$

   **c** $(y - x)^2$

## More simplifying

**3** Simplify

   **a** $p^3 \times p^5$ $\ldots\ldots\ldots$

   **b** $r^2 \times r^7$ $\ldots\ldots\ldots$

   **c** $t^5 \times t^9$ $\ldots\ldots\ldots$

$$p^3 \times p^5 = \overbrace{p \times p \times p}^{3} \times \overbrace{p \times p \times p \times p \times p}^{5}$$

**4** Simplify

   **a** $p^5 \div p^3$ $\ldots\ldots\ldots$

   **b** $r^8 \div r^2$ $\ldots\ldots\ldots$

   **c** $t^9 \div t^7$ $\ldots\ldots\ldots$

$$p^5 \div p^3 = \frac{\overbrace{\cancel{p} \times \cancel{p} \times \cancel{p} \times p \times p}^{5}}{\underbrace{\cancel{p} \times \cancel{p} \times \cancel{p}}_{3}}$$

**5** Simplify

   **a** $(p^2)^3$ $\ldots\ldots\ldots$

   **b** $(r^3)^5$ $\ldots\ldots\ldots$

   **c** $(t^4)^5$ $\ldots\ldots\ldots$

$$3 \times 2 = \square$$
$$(p^2)^3 = \overbrace{(p \times p)}^{2} \times \overbrace{(p \times p)}^{2} \times \overbrace{(p \times p)}^{2}$$

**6** Simplify

**a** $3t^3 \times 4t^5$

$3 \times 4 = \ldots\ldots\ldots$

$t^3 \times t^5 = \ldots\ldots\ldots$

> Multiply the numbers first. Then multiply the variables (letters).

Answer: $\ldots\ldots\ldots$

**b** $4n^6 \times 7n^5$

**c** $3f^4 \times 8f^9$

**d** $\dfrac{20a^5}{4a^3}$

$20 \div 4 = \ldots\ldots\ldots$

$a^5 \div a^3 = \ldots\ldots\ldots$

> Divide the numbers first. Then divide the variables (letters).

Answer: $\ldots\ldots\ldots$

**e** $\dfrac{24c^7}{3c^3}$

**f** $\dfrac{18b^9}{6b}$

**7** Complete

**a** $(4a^5)^2 = 4a^5 \times 4a^5 = \ldots\ldots\ldots$

**b** $(2b^4)^3 = \ldots\ldots\ldots$

**c** $(3c^5)^4 = \ldots\ldots\ldots$

**d** $(2d^3)^2 = \ldots\ldots\ldots$

**e** $\left(\dfrac{r^4}{3}\right)^2 = \dfrac{r^4}{3} \times \dfrac{r^4}{3} = \dfrac{\square}{\square}$

**f** $\left(\dfrac{n^4}{2}\right)^3 = \dfrac{\ldots\ldots}{\ldots\ldots}$

## Expanding and factorising

**8 a** What is the highest common factor (HCF) of 2 and 6? $\ldots\ldots\ldots$

**b** Complete the factorisation:

$2a + 6 = \ldots\ldots (\ldots\ldots + \ldots\ldots)$

> Find the HCF first

**9** Complete the factorisation:

$3a + 15 = \ldots\ldots (\ldots\ldots + \ldots\ldots)$

> The HCF is outside the bracket

**10** Use the grid method to expand these.

**a** $q^2(q + 6)$ ...............

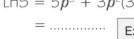

| | $q$ | $6$ |
|---|---|---|
| $q^2$ | $q^3$ | |

$q^2 \times q = q^3$

$q^2 \times 6 = \square$

**b** $k^2(k - 2)$ ...............

| | |
|---|---|
| | |

**c** $n^2(5n + 4)$ ...............

| | |
|---|---|
| | |

**d** $3h^3(1 - 2h)$ ...............

| | $1$ | $-2h$ |
|---|---|---|
| $3h^3$ | | |

**11** Show that this identity is true.

$5p^3 + 3p^2(3p - 2) \equiv 7p^2(2p - 1) + p^2$

LHS $= 5p^3 + 3p^2(3p - 2)$ 　　　　 RHS $= 7p^2(2p - 1) + p^2$

$= $ ...............　　Expand the brackets on the left-hand side and simplify.　　$= $ ...............

$= $ ...............　　Expand the brackets on the right-hand side and simplify.　　$= $ ...............

LHS = RHS

**12** Factorise completely

**a** $2x^2 + 6x^3$ ...............................

**b** $15y^3 - 10y$ ...............................

**c** $8p^2 + 20p$ ...............................

**d** $20r^3 - 50r^2$ ...............................

**e** $18a^4 - 27a^2$ ...............................

**f** $14b^2c^2 + 18bc$ ...............................

Look at the numbers. What is the highest common factor?
Look at the variables. Is there a letter that appears in every term? If yes, what is its lowest power?

## Solving equations

**13** Solve

**a** $6(x + 7) = 15 - 9(1 - 2x)$

**b** $2(4x - 3) = 52 - 3(x + 1)$

**c** $3(x + 5) = 8x + 14 - 3(2x - 1)$

**d** $4(5 + 3x) = 7x + 5 - 2(3 - 4x)$

**Strategy hint**

**Step 1:** Expand the brackets on the right-hand side of the =, and simplify if you can.
**Step 2:** Expand the brackets on the left-hand side of the =.
**Step 3:** Solve the equation.
**Step 4:** Substitute your value of $x$ into the original equation to check.

**1 STEM / Modelling** You can use this formula to find displacement (distance travelled), $s$:

$$s = ut + \tfrac{1}{2}at^2$$

where $s$ = displacement (metres), $u$ = initial velocity (metres per second, m/s)
$t$ = time (seconds) and $a$ = acceleration (metres per second per second, m/s²).

Work out the displacement, $s$, when

**a** $u = 10$, $a = 2$ and $t = 5$       **b** $u = 45$, $a = -10$ and $t = 8$

**2 Reasoning** Here are an equilateral triangle and a square.

**a** Write an expression using brackets for the perimeter of

  **i** the triangle ...............................................................

  **ii** the square. ...............................................................

$2a^2 + 3ab$   $4b^2$       $4b^2 - ab - 3a^2$

**b** Write an expression, in its simplest form, for the difference
between the perimeters of the two shapes when

  **i** the perimeter of the triangle is greater than the perimeter of the square

  **ii** the perimeter of the square is greater than the perimeter of the triangle.

**c** Explain what you notice about your two answers to part **b**.

**3** Factorise completely

  **a** $12x^3 + 15x^2 + 21x$ ...............................................................

  **b** $10a^2 - 15ab + 25a$ ...............................................................

  **c** $18x^2y^2z^3 + 36x^3y^4z^2 - 45x^4y^3z^5$ ...............................................

**Worked
example**

**4 Problem-solving** Both of these expressions have been factorised completely.
Work out the missing terms.

  **a** $10pq + 20p^2 -$ ............... $p^2$ ............... $= 5$ ............... $(2q + 4$ ............... $-3pq)$

  **b** $6$ ............... $y + 15x^2$ ............... $- 21$ ............... $y^2 = 3$ ............... $y(2x + 5 - 7x$ ............... $)$

**5** Find the value of each expression when $a = 3$, $b = -5$ and $c = -4$.

  **a** $(a - c)^2 - 4b$ ...............................................................

  **b** $\sqrt{a^2 + c^2}$ ...............................................................

  **c** $\dfrac{bc - 2a}{7}$ ...............................................................

In part **b**, work out the
value using $a$ and $c$ before
taking the square root.

**6** Find the value of each expression when $x = \tfrac{2}{3}$ and $y = \tfrac{1}{2}$.

  **a** $x^2 - y^2 = \left(\tfrac{2}{3}\right)^2 - \left(\tfrac{1}{2}\right)^2$       **b** $2x^2y$       $\left(\tfrac{2}{3}\right)^2 = \tfrac{4}{9}$

7 **Problem-solving / Reasoning** The diagram shows a parallelogram ABCD.

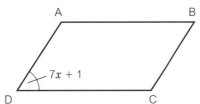

What is the total of two angles next to each other in a parallelogram?

a Write an expression for the size of

  i  angle ABC ........................................    ii  angle BCD. ........................................

b Write an equation using the fact that angle BCD = $4(3x + 2)$ and your answer to part **a i**.

c Solve your equation to find the value of $x$.

d Work out the sizes of the angles in the parallelogram.
  Explain how to check your answers are correct.

8 **Problem-solving** In this spider diagram, the six expressions are all equal to the expression in the middle. Complete the spider diagram.

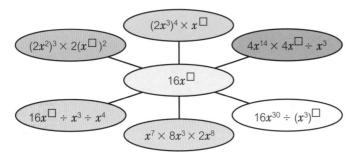

$(2x^3)^4 \times x^{\square}$

$(2x^2)^3 \times 2(x^{\square})^2$

$4x^{14} \times 4x^{\square} \div x^3$

$16x^{\square}$

$16x^{\square} \div x^3 \div x^4$

$16x^{30} \div (x^3)^{\square}$

$x^7 \times 8x^3 \times 2x^8$

9 **Problem-solving**

a Match each expression in the first row (labelled **A** to **G**) to the correct simplified expression in the second row (labelled **1** to **8**).

| A | B | C | D | E | F | G |
|---|---|---|---|---|---|---|
| $x^p \times x^q \times x^r$ | $(x^p)^q \times x^r$ | $x^p \times (x^q)^r$ | $\dfrac{x^p}{x^q \times x^r}$ | $\dfrac{x^p \times x^q}{x^r}$ | $\dfrac{x^p}{(x^q)^r}$ | $\dfrac{(x^p)^q}{x^r}$ |

| 1 | 2 | 3 | 4 | 5 | 6 | 7 | 8 |
|---|---|---|---|---|---|---|---|
| $x^{p+qr}$ | $x^{pq-r}$ | $x^{p+q+r}$ | $x^{p+q-r}$ | $x^{pr-q}$ | $x^{pq+r}$ | $x^{p-q-r}$ | $x^{p-qr}$ |

b There is one simplified expression left over.
  Write the expression that goes with this simplified expression. ...............

**1** Simplify

    **a** $10x^2 - 7x^2$ ............................     **b** $4y^2 + 5y - y^2 - 3y$ ............................

**2** Simplify

    **a** $p^5 \times p^3$ ............................     **b** $\dfrac{q^{12}}{q^4}$ ............................     **c** $(r^3)^5$ ............................

    **d** $e^4 \times e^5 \times e^7$ ............................     **e** $\dfrac{a^3 \times a^7}{a^6}$ ............................     **f** $(n^2)^4$ ............................

**3** Expand

    **a** $x(x^2 - 6x)$ ............................     **b** $3f^2(2f^2 + f - 4)$ ............................

**4** Expand and simplify

    **a** $x(5x + 2) + 2x(3x + 7)$     **b** $5y(2y - 3x + 1) - 3y(y - 2)$

**5** Factorise

    **a** $3d - 12$ ........................     **b** $12e + 16$ ........................     **c** $15 - 10f$ ........................

**6** Which of these are identities?

    **a** $4p + 3p + 6 = 5 - 7p + 1$

    **b** $q + q + 5 = 2 + 5q$

    **c** $3 \times r + 4 \times r - 2 \times 7 = 7(r - 2)$

**7** Factorise completely

    **a** $6x^2 + 18x$ ............................     **b** $25y - 15y^2 + 10y^3$ ............................

**8** Find the value of each expression when $p = 4$, $q = -3$ and $r = 7$.

    **a** $2(p + 5) + 4q$     **b** $5(p - q) - (p + q)$

    **c** $2r^2 + pqr$     **d** $\sqrt{q^2 + r}$

**9** Solve $4(x + 3) = 11 - 7(x - 8)$

**10** Simplify

    **a** $5x^3 \times 2x^4$ ............................     **b** $\dfrac{28y^6}{7y^2}$ ............................     **c** $(3z^5)^2$ ............................

    **d** $(2z^4)^3$ ............................     **e** $\left(\dfrac{r^2}{2}\right)^2$ ............................     **f** $\dfrac{c^3 \times c^8}{c^5}$ ............................

**1** Work out the area of each parallelogram.

**a**

6 cm
5 cm
10 cm

**b**

2 m
6.5 m
1 m

▶ Area of a parallelogram = $bh$

= 10 × 5 = ...............

Area of a parallelogram
= base length × perpendicular height
= $b × h$
= $bh$
The perpendicular height is the height
measured at right angles to the base.

**2** Work out the missing measurement for this parallelogram.

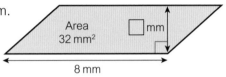

Area
32 mm²     ☐ mm

8 mm

**3** Work out the area of each triangle.

**a**

5 cm
8 cm

**b**

8 cm
60 mm
12 cm

**c**

2 m
4 m
80 cm

Area of a triangle
= $\frac{1}{2} bh$

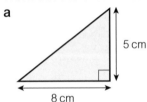

Area = $\frac{1}{2} bh$

= $\frac{1}{2}$ × ............... × ............... = ...............

Make sure all the lengths
for each shape are in the
same units.

**4** Work out the missing measurement for this triangle.

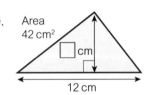

Area
42 cm²     ☐ cm

12 cm

Substitute the values
you know into the
formula for the area,
then solve the equation.

**5** **Problem-solving** Sachita makes a flag from black and grey cloth. The three triangles are
isosceles. Work out the total area of cloth Sachita needs.

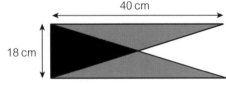

40 cm
18 cm

**6** Work out the area of each trapezium.

**a**

6 cm
8 cm
14 cm

**b**

8 cm
6 mm
5 mm

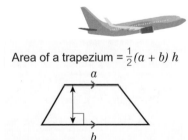

Area of a trapezium = $\frac{1}{2}(a + b) h$

$a$
$b$

**Check**     Tick each box as your
**confidence** in this
30          topic improves.

☹ ☺ ☺
☐ ☐ ☐

**Need extra help?** Go to page 38 and tick
the boxes next to Q1, 2 and 4. Then try them
once you've finished 4.1–4.8.

# Area of compound shapes

**1** Calculate the total area of each shape.

**a**

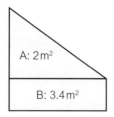

A: 2 m²

B: 3.4 m²

**b**

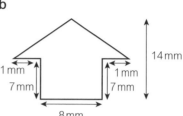

A: 14 cm²

B: 52 cm²

**2** Calculate the area of each shape.

**a**

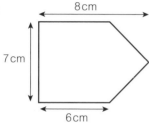

8 cm

7 cm

6 cm

**b**

14 mm

1 mm  1 mm

7 mm  7 mm

8 mm

**3 Real** Kasia wants someone to paint the side of her house. It looks like this.

**a** What is the area of the side of her house? Give your answer in square metres.

3 m

4 m

10 m

Split the wall into a rectangle and a triangle.

Danilo charges $4.50 per square metre for painting.

**b** How much will Danilo charge for painting the side of the house?

**4 Problem-solving** Work out the shaded area of each shape.

**a**

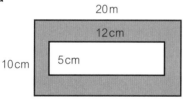

20 m

12 cm

10 cm   5 cm

**b**

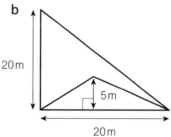

20 m

20 m

5 m

20 m

**5 Real / Problem-solving** Three congruent trapeziums and two congruent parallelograms are pressed out of a metal strip. What area of the metal strip is unused?

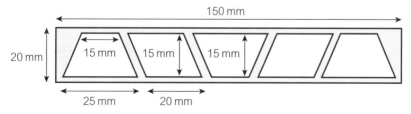

150 mm

20 mm   15 mm   15 mm   15 mm

25 mm   20 mm

**Check**  Tick each box as your **confidence** in this topic improves.      **Need extra help?** Go to page 38 and tick the box next to Q3. Then try it once you've finished 4.1–4.8.

31

**1** Sketch a **net** for each cuboid.

**a**

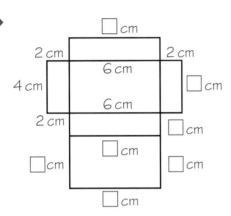

4 cm
2 cm
6 cm

**b**

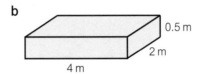

0.5 m
2 m
4 m

A **net** is a 2D shape that folds to make a 3D solid.

Guided

☐ cm
2 cm    2 cm
6 cm
4 cm              ☐ cm
6 cm
2 cm              ☐ cm
☐ cm
☐ cm              ☐ cm
☐ cm

For a sketch you should use a ruler and a pencil, but you don't need to measure the lengths accurately.

**2** Look at these nets.

**A**

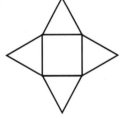

**B**

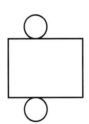

**C**

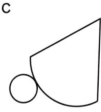

Which one folds to make   **a** a cone ....... **b** a square-based pyramid ....... **c** a cylinder? .......

**3** Write down the number of **faces**, **edges** and **vertices** in this cuboid.

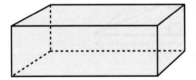

faces ...............

edges ...............

vertices ...............

3D solids have **faces** (flat surfaces), **edges** (where two faces meet) and **vertices** (corners). A single corner is called a **vertex**.

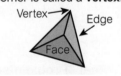

Vertex
Edge
Face

**4** **Problem-solving** Look at this cuboid.
You can cut a cuboid into two equal parts.
Sketch the new 3D solids you would make if you cut it

**a** horizontally          **b** vertically          **c** diagonally.

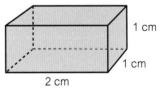

1 cm
1 cm
2 cm

**Check**      Tick each box as your **confidence** in this topic improves.

**Need extra help?** Go to page 38 and tick the box next to Q5. Then try it once you've finished 4.1–4.8.

32

**1** The diagrams show a cube and its net.
Work out the surface area of the cube.

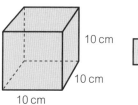
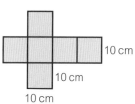

10 cm
10 cm
10 cm
10 cm
10 cm
10 cm

The surface area of a 3D shape is the total area of all its faces.

**2** What is the surface area of each cube?

**a**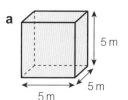

5 m
5 m
5 m

**b** a 2 mm by 2 mm by 2 mm cube

**c** a cube with edge length 1 cm

**3** Work out the surface area of each cuboid.

**a**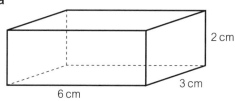

2 cm
3 cm
6 cm

**b**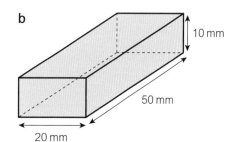

10 mm
50 mm
20 mm

**Guided**

Surface area
Area of top face = 6 × 3 = 18 cm²
Area of front face = 6 × ....... = ....... cm²
Area of side face = ....... × ....... = ....... cm²
Sum of 3 faces = ....... + ....... + ....... = ....... cm²
Total surface area = 2 × ....... = ....... cm²

**4 Problem-solving** A cube has a surface area of 96 cm².

**a** What is the area of each face? ................................................................................................

**b** What is the length of one edge? ................................................................................................

**5 Real / Problem-solving** Farouq wants to paint the outside of this metal container.
He cannot paint underneath the container.
He has 4 cans of paint. Each can covers 20 m².
Will this be enough? Explain your answer.

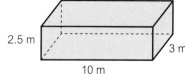

2.5 m
3 m
10 m

**Worked example**

**Check** Tick each box as your **confidence** in this topic improves.

**Need extra help?** Go to page 39 and tick the box next to Q6. Then try it once you've finished 4.1–4.8.

33

**Guided**

**1** A cube has a side length of 5 cm. What is the **volume** of the cube?

Volume of a cube = side length ($l$) cubed = $l^3 = 5^3 = $ .............. cm³

**2 Problem-solving** A cube has a surface area of 150 cm².

   **a** What is the area of one face? ....................................................

   **b** What is the length of one side? ................................................

   **c** What is the volume of the cube? ................................................

> **Strategy hint**
>
> Sketch a cube.

The **volume** of a solid shape is the amount of 3D space it takes up. The units of volume are cubic units (e.g. mm³, cm³, m³).

**3** Calculate the volume of each cuboid.

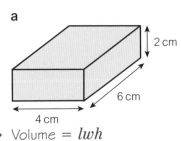

**a**

2 cm

6 cm

4 cm

Volume = $lwh$

= 6 × 4 × 2

= .............. cm³

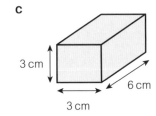

**b**

5 m

4 m

1.5 m

**c**

3 cm

6 cm

3 cm

Volume of a cuboid
= length × width × height
= $l × w × h$
= $lwh$

height

width

length

**4** Complete these conversions.

   **a** 0.25 litres = .............. cm³

   **b** 5 cm³ = .............. m$l$

   **c** .............. litres = 5125 cm³

1 litre   0.25 litre

×1000                   ×1000

1000 cm³   ☐ cm³

The capacity of a container is how much it can hold. The units of capacity are cm³, millilitres (m$l$) and litres ($l$).
• 1 millilitre (m$l$) = 1 cm³
• 1 litre ($l$) = 1000 cm³

**5 Real / Reasoning** For a drive through Spain in the summer, Greg buys a car-fridge with internal measurements 25 cm by 20 cm by 30 cm.

   **a** Work out the capacity in cm³. ...........................................

   **b** Work out the capacity in litres. ...........................................

Greg estimates that he will be able to fit seven 2-litre bottles of water in the fridge.

   **c** Explain why he might be wrong.

**6 Problem-solving** A 10 cm by 10 cm by 10 cm cube has a 5 cm by 5 cm square hole cut right through it. What is the volume of the remaining solid?

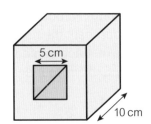

5 cm

10 cm

What is the volume of the piece cut out of the cube?

**Check**   Tick each box as your **confidence** in this topic improves.

**Need extra help?** Go to page 39 and tick the box next to Q7. Then try it once you've finished 4.1–4.8.

34

**1** Which unit of area would be sensible for measuring

   **a** the area of a smartphone ................

   **b** the area of Italy ................................

   **c** the area of a netball court? ...............

> It is important to be able to choose the most suitable metric units for measuring. Some of the metric units that you already know are
> - mm, cm, m, km (length)
> - $mm^2$, $cm^2$, $m^2$, $km^2$, hectares (area)

**2 Real** A rectangular runway measures 2.4 km by 250 m. How many hectares is this?

> Convert km to m and then $m^2$ to hectares. A hectare is 10 000 $m^2$.

Area = 2.4 km × 250 m = 2400 × 250 = .............. $m^2$

Number of hectares = .............. ÷ .............. = ..............

**3** These squares are the same size.

   **a** Write in the missing measurements.

   **b** Work out the area of

     **i** square A ............... $cm^2$    **ii** square B ............... $mm^2$

   **c** Complete these sentences.

     **i** To convert from $cm^2$ to $mm^2$ ................................ by ..............

     **ii** To convert from $mm^2$ to $cm^2$ ................................ by ..............

**4** Complete these conversions.

   **a** $8 cm^2 = 8 \times 10^2 = 800 mm^2$

   **b** $57500 cm^2 =$ .............. $m^2$

   **c** .............. $cm^2 = 950 mm^2$

   **d** .............. $m^2 = 8.5 km^2$

   **e** $0.2 m^2 =$ .............. $cm^2$

   **f** $4500 m^2 =$ .............. $km^2$

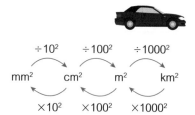

$$mm^2 \xrightarrow{\div 10^2} cm^2 \xrightarrow{\div 100^2} m^2 \xrightarrow{\div 1000^2} km^2$$
$$mm^2 \xleftarrow{\times 10^2} cm^2 \xleftarrow{\times 100^2} m^2 \xleftarrow{\times 1000^2} km^2$$

**Worked example**

**5 Problem-solving** The base of a swimming pool is to be tiled using small square tiles of side length 2 cm.
The base is a 12 m by 4 m rectangle. How many tiles are needed?

**6** Complete these conversions.

   **a** $12 cm^3 =$ .............. $mm^3$     **b** .............. $cm^3 = 66 mm^3$

   **c** $1.75 m^3 =$ .............. $cm^3$     **d** .............. $m^3 = 125000 cm^3$

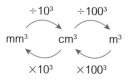

$$mm^3 \xrightarrow{\div 10^3} cm^3 \xrightarrow{\div 100^3} m^3$$
$$mm^3 \xleftarrow{\times 10^3} cm^3 \xleftarrow{\times 100^3} m^3$$

**7 Problem-solving** A toy manufacturer needs to ship (transport) 100 000 toys from China to the USA. Each toy is in a box measuring 25 cm × 25 cm × 10 cm, and the shipping containers measure 12 m × 2.5 m × 2.5 m.
How many containers does the company need to transport all 100 000 toys at once?

---

**Check**    Tick each box as your **confidence** in this topic improves.

**Need extra help?** Go to page 39 and tick the boxes next to Q9 and 10. Then try them once you've finished 4.1–4.8.

**1** Draw the **plan**, the **front elevation** and the **side elevation** of the solid.

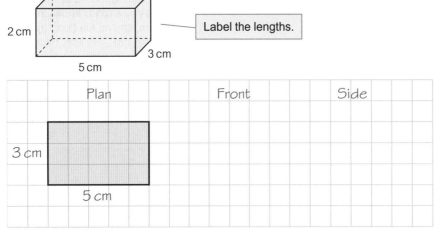

Label the lengths.

2 cm
3 cm
5 cm

Plan | Front | Side

3 cm

5 cm

The **plan** is the view from above the object.
The **front elevation** is the view of the front of the object.
The **side elevation** is the view of the side of the object.

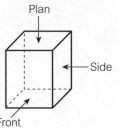

Plan
Side
Front

**2** These solids, drawn on an isometric grid, are made from centimetre square cubes. Draw the plan, the front elevation and the side elevation of each solid.

**a** 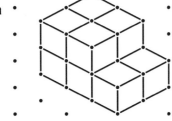  **b**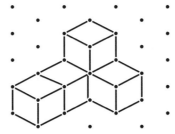

**Worked example**

**3 Problem-solving** Here are the plan, front and side elevations of an irregular 3D solid.
If you have them, use cubes to make the solid.
Then draw it on the isometric grid below.

Plan | Front | Side

**Check** Tick each box as your **confidence** in this topic improves.

**Need extra help?** Go to page 39 and tick the box next to Q8. Then try it once you've finished 4.1–4.8.

**1 Problem-solving** A medicine bottle says, 'Take three 5 ml spoonfuls three times per day.' The bottle contains 0.2 litres. Ranjeev has to take the medicine for 5 days. Is there enough medicine in the bottle? Explain your answer.

> Units of capacity and units of volume can be converted.
> 1 ml = 1 cm³, so 1 litre = 1000 cm³

**2** Ian is using his calculator to solve some problems.
Which value, A, B or C, should he enter for each measure?

a  5 m 5 cm (in metres)      **A** 5.5      **B** 5.05      **C** 5.005
b  444 ml (in litres)        **A** 4.44     **B** 0.444     **C** 0.0444
c  3 kg 30 g (in grams)      **A** 33000    **B** 30030     **C** 3030
d  2 tonnes 2 kg (in tonnes) **A** 2.2      **B** 2.02      **C** 2.002
e  1 litre 100 ml (in cm³)   **A** 1100     **B** 11        **C** 0.0011

> For part **d**, use
> 1 tonne (t) = 1000 kg

**3** Work out the volume of this shape.

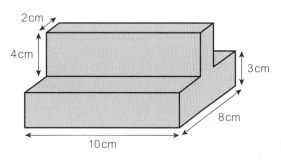

**4 Problem-solving** The diagram shows the dimensions of a small box in the shape of a cube.
A large box has dimensions 50 cm by 40 cm by 10 cm.
How many small boxes will fit into the large box?

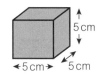

> **Strategy hint**
> Start by working out how many small boxes will fit along the length of the large box.

**5 Problem-solving** A cuboid has a height of 7 cm and a width of 9 cm. Its volume is 661.5 cm³.
Work out the surface area of the cuboid.

> Use the volume to work out the length of the cuboid first.

**6 Problem-solving** The white triangle has an area of 1.5 m².
The area of the purple triangle is $\frac{1}{5}$ smaller than the area of the white triangle.
Work out the height of the purple triangle.

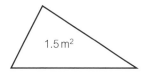
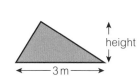

**Check** Tick each box as your **confidence** in this topic improves. ☹ 😐 ☺

**Need extra help?** Go to page 39 and tick the box next to Q11. Then try it once you've finished 4.1–4.8.

37

## Area of shapes

**1** Use the formula
area of a triangle = $\frac{1}{2}$ × base length × perpendicular height
to work out the area of each triangle.

The base length and the perpendicular height must be at right angles (90°) to each other.
For part **a**, area = $\frac{1}{2}$ × $b$ × $h$ = $\frac{1}{2}$ × 4 × 3 = 2 × 3 = □ m²

**a**

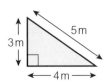

**b**

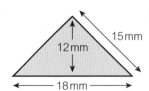

**2** Calculate the area of the parallelogram.

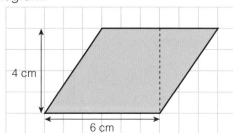

Imagine making the parallelogram into a rectangle by moving part of the shape to the other side.

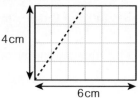

**3** Work out the area of this shape.

> Area of rectangle = $l \times w$ = 24 × ............
> = ............ m²
> Area of triangle = $\frac{1}{2} \times b \times h = \frac{1}{2}$ × 24 × ............
> = ............ m²

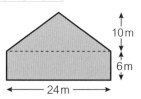

Area of shape = area of rectangle + area of triangle = ............ + ............ = ............ m²

**4** Calculate the area of the trapezium.

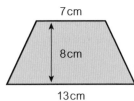

> Area = $\frac{1}{2}(a + b)h$
> = $\frac{1}{2}$ × ( ....... + ....... ) × .......
> = $\frac{1}{2}$ × ....... × .......
> = ....... cm²

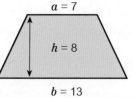

**Worked example**

## Working with 3D solids

**5** Which of these nets will fold to make a triangular prism?

**a** 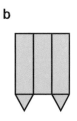 **b** 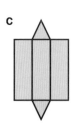 **c** **d**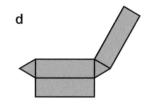

You could draw the shapes and cut them out. Try to fold each one into a triangular prism.

**6** Complete the table to find the surface area of the cuboid.

| Face | Area |
|---|---|
| Top | $5 \times 2 = 10\,cm^2$ |
| Bottom | |
| Front | $5 \times 3 = 15\,cm^2$ |
| Back | |
| Left | $2 \times 3 = 6\,cm^2$ |
| Right | |
| **Total surface area** | |

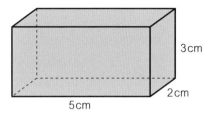

**7** Calculate the volume of the cuboid in Q6.

Volume $= l \times w \times h$

$= 2 \times \underline{\quad} \times \underline{\quad}$

$= \underline{\quad} cm^3$

**8** Draw the plan and the front and side elevations of the triangular prism.

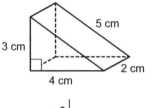

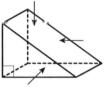

## Measures of area and volume

**9 a** Work out the area of the rectangle in $m^2$.

Area $= \underline{\quad} \times \underline{\quad} = \underline{\quad}$

**b** Convert the area of the rectangle to $cm^2$.

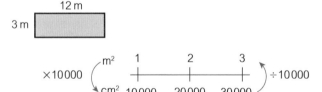

**10** Complete these conversions.

**a i** $8\,cm^3 = \underline{\quad}\,mm^3$  **ii** $\underline{\quad}\,cm^3 = 22\,500\,mm^3$

**b i** $0.03\,m^3 = \underline{\quad}\,cm^3$  **ii** $\underline{\quad}\,m^3 = 6.5$ million $cm^3$

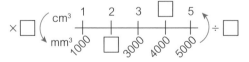

**11** A cube has a surface area of $54\,cm^2$.

**a** Find the length of each side of the cube.

How many faces does a cube have? What is the area of each face?

**b** Work out the volume of the cube.

**Guided**

1 The volume of water in a swimming pool in the shape of a cuboid is 120 m³. The pool is 15 m long and 5 m wide. The water comes to 12 cm from the top of the pool.

a Calculate the depth of water in the pool.

Volume = base × height × width

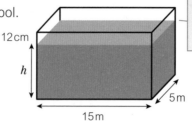

12 cm

h

15 m

5 m

Sketch the water in the pool. Put the measurements you know on your sketch.

**Worked example**

b How much more water is required to fill the pool to 2 cm from the top?

2 **Problem-solving** The diagram shows a badge in the shape of a right-angled triangle.
What percentage of the badge is white?
Write your answer to the nearest whole number.

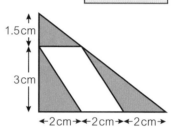

1.5 cm

3 cm

←2 cm→←2 cm→←2 cm→

Percentage of white = $\frac{\text{area of white}}{\text{area of triangle}}$ × 100
Work out the areas of the triangle and the parallelogram.

3 **Problem-solving** This parallelogram and this trapezium have the same area.
What is the perpendicular height of the trapezium?

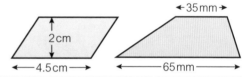

2 cm

←4.5 cm→

←35 mm→

←65 mm→

**Strategy hint**

Make sure all measurements are in the same units.

**Worked example**

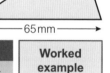

4 Work out the shaded area of each shape.

a
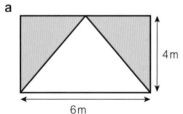
4 m

6 m

b
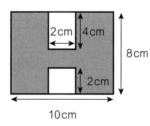
2 cm 4 cm
8 cm
2 cm
10 cm

c
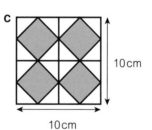
10 cm
10 cm

5 **Reasoning** Look at this cuboid.

a Calculate the volume of the cuboid. ..............................................

b Calculate the surface area of the cuboid.

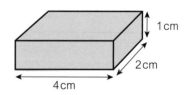
1 cm
2 cm
4 cm

c How can four of these cuboids be put together to make a cuboid with the smallest surface area?

6 A cube has a volume of 27cm³. The cube is cut into three equal cuboids.
What is the surface area of one of the cuboids?

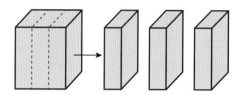

7 Calculate the volume of each solid.

a

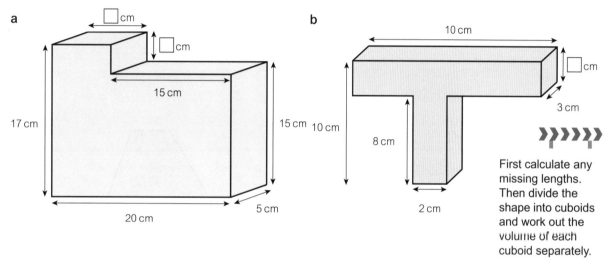

☐ cm

☐ cm

15 cm

17 cm

20 cm

5 cm

15 cm 10 cm

b

10 cm

☐ cm

3 cm

8 cm

2 cm

》》》》》

First calculate any missing lengths. Then divide the shape into cuboids and work out the volume of each cuboid separately.

8 Calculate the surface area of this triangular prism.

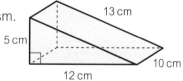

13 cm

5 cm

12 cm

10 cm

**1** Work out the area of this shape.

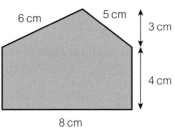

**2** For each shape work out **i** the volume **ii** the surface area.

**a**

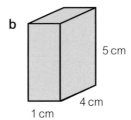

**b**

**3** Work out the area of each shape.

**a** 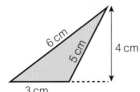 **b** 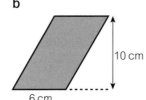 **c**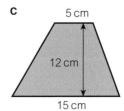

**4** The diagram shows a cuboid.

**a** Draw the cuboid on the isometric grid.

On the square grid, draw

**b** the plan of the cuboid

**c** the front elevation of the cuboid

**d** the side elevation of the cuboid.

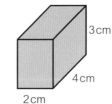

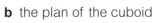

**5** Complete these conversions.

**a** $7.2\,m^3$ = ................... $cm^3$  **b** ................... $cm^3$ = $9900\,mm^3$  **c** $630\,ml$ = ................... $cm^3$

**6** The diagram shows a shape made up of cuboids. Work out

**a** the volume

**b** the surface area.

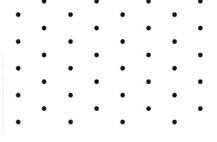

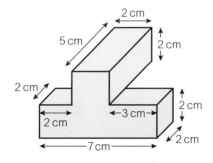

When you have finished the Unit test, fill in the **Progression chart** on page 111.

**Guided**

**1 Real / Problem-solving** This graph can be used to convert approximately between pounds (lb) and kilograms (kg).

**Conversion graph for pounds and kilograms**

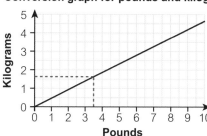

When two quantities are in direct proportion
* plotting them as a graph gives a straight line through the origin (0, 0)
* when one quantity is zero, the other quantity is also zero
* when one quantity doubles, so does the other.

> Draw a vertical line from 3.5 pounds to the graph.
> From this point on the graph draw a horizontal line to the 'Kilograms' axis.

**a** Are pounds and kilograms in direct proportion? ...............

**b** Complete: $3\frac{1}{2}$ pounds ≈ ............... kilograms

**c** Complete: 4 kilograms ≈ ............... pounds

**d** Which is heavier, 1 kilogram or 2 pounds? ...............................

**2 Real** A phone company charges a monthly fee for line rental and an amount per minute for phone calls. This graph shows the costs.

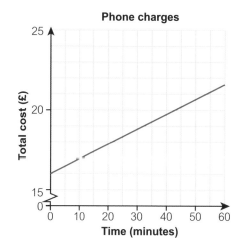

**a** Are the call time and the total cost in direct proportion? Explain your answer.

**b** Shaun spent 50 minutes on the phone in March. How much was his March bill? ...............

**c** In April Shaun's bill was £17.80. How long had he been on the phone? ...............

**d** What is Shaun's monthly charge for line rental? ...............

**3 STEM** In a science experiment, the volume of a gas was measured at different temperatures. The table shows some of the results.

| Temperature (°C) | 0 | 25 | 50 | 75 | 100 |
|---|---|---|---|---|---|
| Volume (cm³) | 114 | 124 | 134 | 144 | 154 |

**a** Plot a line graph for these values.

**b** Are temperature and the volume of the gas in direct proportion? Explain your answer.

**4 Real** Are these in direct proportion? Write yes or no.

**a** US dollars ($) and pounds (£) ...............

**b** The weight of a person and their age, from 0 to 20 years ...............

**c** Cost and hours worked by a plumber who charges a call-out fee ...............

**d** Pints and litres ...............

**Strategy hint**

Sketch or visualise a graph.

**Check** Tick each box as your **confidence** in this topic improves.

**Need extra help?** Go to page 48 and tick the boxes next to Q1 and 2. Then try them once you've finished 5.1–5.5.

**1 Finance** The **line graph** shows the share price of a bank on the first Monday of each month in 2013.

**Share prices on the first Monday of each month in 2013**

**a** Describe the overall trend in the share price during 2013.

> **Line graphs** can help you identify trends in the data. The trend is the general direction of the change, ignoring the individual ups and downs.

**b** What was the difference in share price between January and December?

**c** In which month did the price reach a minimum before increasing again?

**d** Carla bought 120 shares at the beginning of March and sold them at the beginning of November. What was her profit?

> The profit is the selling price minus the buying price.

**2 Finance** The graph shows the cost of sending a medium sized package by first class post.

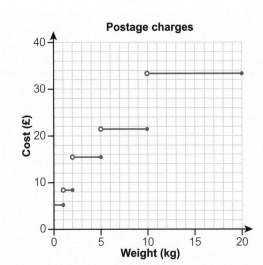

**Postage charges**

**a** How much does a parcel weighing 7 kg cost to post?

> The open circles show that the lower value of each graph line is not included in the interval.

**b** How much does a parcel weighing 10 kg cost to post?

**c** Helen paid £33.40 to post her parcel. How heavy was it?

**Check** Tick each box as your **confidence** in this topic improves.

☹ 😐 ☺

**Need extra help?** Go to page 49 and tick the box next to Q5. Then try it once you've finished 5.1–5.5.

44

**1** Sam walks from his house to Will's house. On his way home he stops at a shop.
The **distance–time graph** shows his journey there and back.

Sam's journey

A **distance–time graph** represents a journey. The vertical axis represents the distance from the starting point. The horizontal axis represents the time taken.

**a** How far away does Will live from Sam? ...............

**b** How long does Sam stay at Will's house? ...............

**c** How long does Sam spend at the shop on his way home? ...............

**d** How long does it take Sam to get from his house to Will's house? ...............

**e** How long does it take Sam to get from Will's house to the shop? ...............

**2** Lisa is driving from Manchester to London for a meeting.
She records her distance from home every half hour.

| Time | 9.30 am | 10 am | 10.30 am | 11 am | 11.30 am | 12 pm | 12.30 pm | 1 pm | 1.30 pm |
|---|---|---|---|---|---|---|---|---|---|
| Distance from home (miles) | 0 | 30 | 60 | 95 | 130 | 130 | 165 | 190 | 200 |

**a** Show this information on a graph.

**b** When did Lisa stop for a break?

**c** Lisa spent most of the journey on the motorway before arriving at the outskirts of London. At what time do you think Lisa arrived at the outskirts of London?

**d** Calculate Lisa's average **speed** between

  **i** 9.30am and 11.30am

  **ii** 1pm and 1.30pm.

Compound measures combine measures of two different quantities. **Speed** is a measure of distance travelled and time taken. It can be measured in metres per second (m/s), kilometres per hour (km/h) or miles per hour (mph).

You can calculate average **speed** if you know the distance and the time.

Speed = $\frac{\text{distance}}{\text{time}}$ or $S = \frac{D}{T}$

**Worked example**

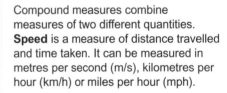

**Check** Tick each box as your **confidence** in this topic improves.

**Need extra help?** Go to page 48 and tick the boxes next to Q3 and 4. Then try them once you've finished 5.1–5.5.

1 **Finance / Modelling** The graph shows the value of a motorbike.

   a Estimate the value of the motorbike when it is 3 years old.

   b Between which two years did the value change the most?

   c Between which two years did the value change the least?

   d When is the motorbike worth 50% of its original value?

   e Will the value of the motorbike ever reach zero?

A rate of change graph shows how a quantity changes over time.

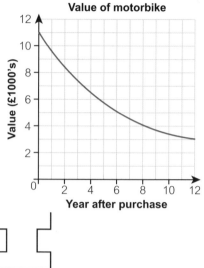

2 Water is poured into this container at a steady rate.

   a Which fills faster, the wider parts or the narrow part?

   b Circle the graph which shows how the depth of water in this container changes over time.

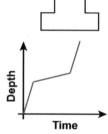

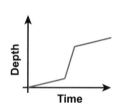

3 The five containers below are filled with water.

   a Match each container to its graph (one has no graph).

For a linear relationship the points on a graph form a straight line.
When the points are not in a straight line, the relationship is non-linear.

Is the rate of water flow changing all the time?
Is it getting slower or faster?

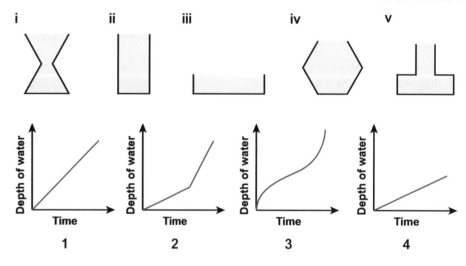

   b Sketch a graph for the container that has no graph.

**Check** Tick each box as your **confidence** in this topic improves.

☹ 😐 ☺

**Need extra help?** Go to page 49 and tick the box next to Q6. Then try them once you've finished 5.1–5.5.

1 **Real** The graph shows the price of petrol.

a What is unusual about the vertical scale on the graph?

b Use the values in the table to draw a graph with a vertical scale of 10p, 20p, ...

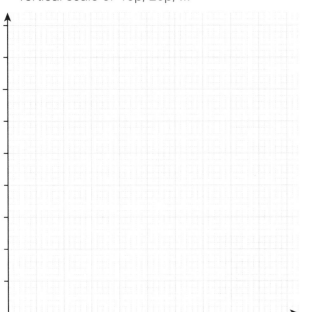

**Price of petrol per litre**

c Describe the trend in the price of petrol between 1900 and 2000.

| Year | Cost |
|------|------|
| 1900 | 1p |
| 1910 | 1.2p |
| 1930 | 1.5p |
| 1940 | 2.2p |
| 1950 | 3.3p |
| 1960 | 5.1p |
| 1970 | 7.3p |
| 1980 | 28p |
| 1990 | 47p |
| 2000 | 88p |

2 **Finance** These two graphs show the same figures for average house prices in England.

a Ant says, 'House prices increased rapidly between 2006 and 2010.' Which graph is he using? ..............

b His estate agent says, 'House prices have almost been constant.' Which graph is she using? ..............

c What is the actual increase in the average house price between 2006 and 2013?

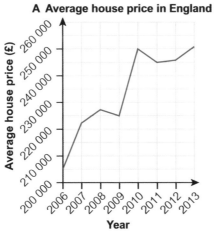

**A Average house price in England**

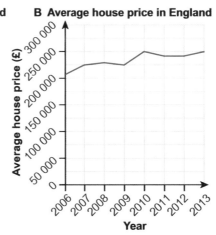

**B Average house price in England**

**Check** Tick each box as your **confidence** in this topic improves. ☹ 😐 ☺

**Need extra help?** Go to page 49 and tick the box next to Q7. Then try them once you've finished 5.1–5.5.

47

## Direct proportion

1 **Real** Circle the graphs which show direct proportion.

Which graphs show a straight line through the origin?

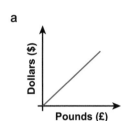
a

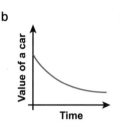
b

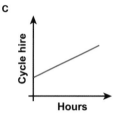
c

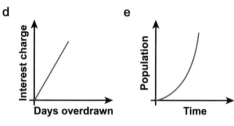
d          e

2 The graph shows the conversion between pounds (£) and euros (€).

a When Dave is holidaying in France, he spends €6 in a shop. How much is this in pounds? ...............

b Dave spends €12 on a meal. How much is this in pounds? ...............

**Worked example**

c When Dave returns from holiday, he changes his euros back into pounds at the bank. He gets £12. How many euros did he change? ...............

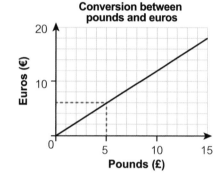

## Distance–time graphs

3 Ian travelled by car to visit his sister in hospital.
He left home at 1 pm.
He drove 60 km in 45 minutes.
He stayed at the hospital for 1 hour 30 minutes and then drove directly home, arriving home at 4.15 pm.

a Draw a distance–time graph to show Ian's journey.

b Give your graph a title.

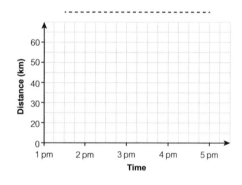

4 The Bradshaws travel home after a stay with relatives.

a How many times did they stop during the journey? ...............

b How many miles does one small square on the vertical axis represent? ...............

c What is the total distance from their relatives to home?

d How many minutes does one small square on the horizontal axis represent? ...............

e What is the total time to travel home? ...............

f In which section were they travelling fastest? ...............

g Work out the average speed in miles per hour using the formula

$$\text{average speed} = \frac{\text{total distance in miles}}{\text{total time in hours}} = \text{...............}$$

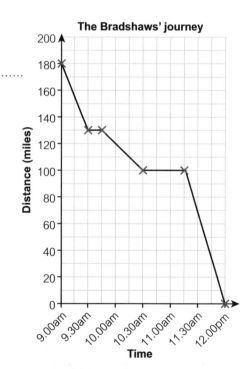

The Bradshaws' journey

## Real-life graphs

**5 Finance** The graph shows the average cost of fish and chips in the UK since 1950.

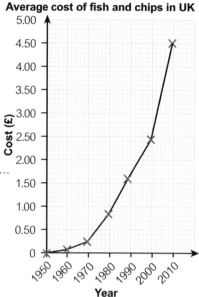

**Average cost of fish and chips in UK**

a How much does one square on the vertical axis represent? ...............

b What was the average cost of fish and chips in

   i 1970 ...............     ii 2000? ...............

c In which year was the average cost of fish and chips 83p? .........

**6** The graphs show the power output of four different wind turbines as the wind speed increases.
Match each description to the correct graph.

a Turbine A's power output increases steadily. ...............

b Turbine B's power output increases steadily at wind speeds up to 30 mph. At wind speeds over 30 mph the increase is steady but more rapid. ...............

c Turbine C produces a little power to start with but gradually increases power output. ...............

d Turbine D produces a little power to start with, gradually increases power output until wind speeds reach 50 mph, then power output remains constant. ...

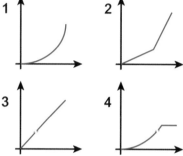

**7 Finance** These two graphs show the same figures for the average price of unleaded petrol in the UK from 17 December 2013 to 31 January 2014.

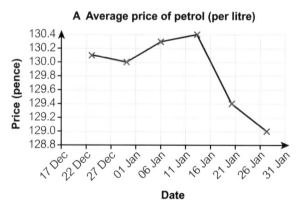

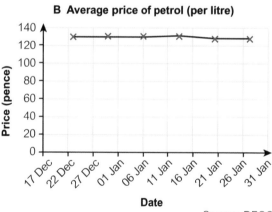

Source: DECC

a The Environment Agency reports, 'Petrol prices are almost constant'. Which graph are they using? ...............

b A lorry driver says, 'Petrol prices fell at the end of December, rose after the beginning of the year and then decreased.' Which graph is he using? ...............

c What was the actual decrease in petrol price between 13 January and 27 January 2014?

d Work out the percentage decrease in the price of petrol between 23 December 2013 and 27 January 2014.

$$\text{Percentage decrease} = \frac{\text{actual decrease}}{\text{original amount}} \times 100$$

**1 Modelling** The graph shows the average rainfall and maximum temperature in Manchester.

a On average, which month is

  i the warmest ...............

  ii the driest? ...............

Kerry is planning a trip to Manchester. She is considering going in either April or October.

b Use the graph to work out the temperature in

  i April ............  ii October. ............

c Use the graph to work out the rainfall in

  i April ............  ii October. ............

d In which month should Kerry go to Manchester? ...............

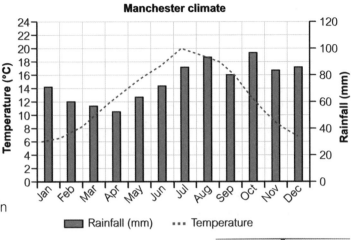

**Manchester climate**

■ Rainfall (mm)   ••• Temperature

**2** A motorsport driver travelled approximately 312.5 miles in $2\frac{1}{2}$ hours. Calculate his average speed in miles per hour.

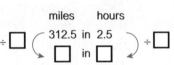

**3 Modelling** Dev travelled from Manchester to Edinburgh for a meeting, a distance of 210 miles. His average speed on the way there was 60 mph and on the way back it was 70 mph. Dev's meeting lasted $2\frac{1}{2}$ hours.

a Draw a distance–time graph to show this information.

b Calculate Dev's average travelling speed for the journey.

**4** Work out the average speed of each of these journeys.

a A plane travels 216 miles from London to Paris in 1 hour 15 minutes.

b A tortoise walks 348 metres in 1 hour 40 minutes.

**5 Real** The graph shows the volumes of petrol and diesel delivered in the UK between 1970 and 2012.

a Approximately how many litres of diesel were delivered in the UK in

  i 1970 ...............  ii 2010? ...............

b Describe the trend in the amount of diesel delivered in the UK since 1970.

c Describe the trend in the amount of petrol delivered in the UK since 1970.

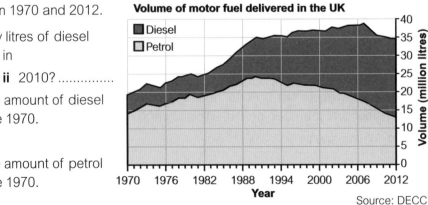

**Volume of motor fuel delivered in the UK**

■ Diesel
□ Petrol

Source: DECC

d On the whole, is more or less motor fuel being delivered in the UK? Explain your answer.

**6 Modelling** The Waltons are planning a city holiday and are choosing between Rome and New York.

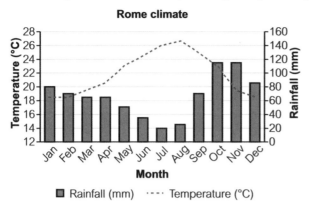

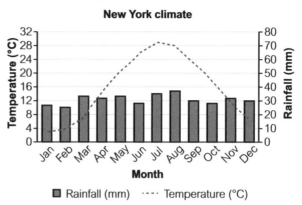

**a** What is the temperature in August in

   **i** Rome ..............       **ii** New York? ..............

**b** What is the rainfall in January in

   **i** Rome ..............       **ii** New York? ..............

**c** Explain what feature of these graphs makes it difficult to compare the weather in Rome and New York.

**d** Mrs Walton says, 'The graphs show that New York is always warmer and wetter than Rome.' Is she correct? Explain your answer.

**7 Real** These graphs show the numbers of people using a social media website per month.

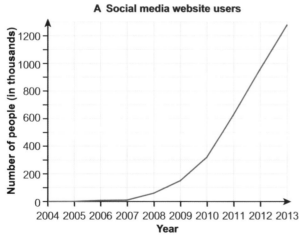

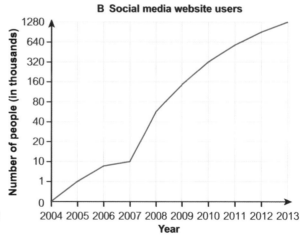

**a** In the Graph A, what does one square on the vertical axis represent? ..............

**b** Describe how the vertical scale changes on Graph B.

**c** In which year was the website launched? ..............

**d** How many people used the website in

   **i** 2005 ..............       **ii** 2010? ..............

**e** Which graph was the most useful for answering each question in part **d**? ..............

1 Tara cycles to a shopping centre.
On the way home she stops to buy lunch.

a How long was Tara at the
shopping centre? ...............

b Which was the slowest part of
the journey?

**Tara's journey**

c What was her average speed from the
shopping centre to home?

2 The graphs show the races swum by four different swimmers.
Match each description to the correct graph.

a Swimmer A starts off fast and gradually slows down. ...............

b Swimmer B swims at a constant speed throughout the race. ...............

c Swimmer C starts off slowly and then gradually
increases speed. ...............

d Swimmer D swims at a fast constant speed, and then at a slower
constant speed. ...............

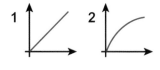

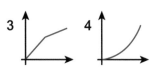

3 A plumber charges a call-out fee and then
an hourly rate.
Some of his charges are shown in the table.

| Time (hours) | 2 | 4 | 5 |
|---|---|---|---|
| Cost (£) | 80 | 130 | 155 |

a Draw a graph to show this information. Plot Time on the horizontal
axis and Cost on the vertical axis. Use suitable scales.

b What is the plumber's call-out charge? ...............

c What is his hourly charge? ...............

d Are time and cost in direct proportion? Explain.

4 Circle the graphs which show direct proportion.

a     b 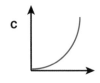    c    d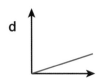

5 The graph shows the average annual salary
for a particular job over the last 50 years.

a Estimate the average salary

   i at present ............ ii 20 years ago ............

   iii 30 years ago. ...............

b Describe the trend in salaries over the last 50 years.

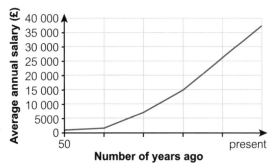

**Guided**

**1** Round these numbers to 1 decimal place.

**a** 4.72 = 4.7 ———

> 2 is less than 5 so round down.

**b** 8.44 ...............

**c** 82.96 ...............

**d** 56.75 ...............

> To round a decimal to 1 decimal place (1 d.p.), look at the digit in the second decimal place. If the digit is less than 5, round down. If the digit is 5 or more, round up. Write the number in the first decimal place, even if the number is 0.

**2** **Real** Alistair scores 17, 16, 17 and 25 runs in his first four innings of 2014. Calculate his mean score. Round your answer to 1 decimal place.

**3** **Problem-solving** Elaine writes an answer of 8.7 correct to 1 decimal place. What could her number have been, correct to 2 decimal places? ...............

**Guided**

**4** Round these numbers to 2 decimal places.

**a** 12.368 = 12.37 ——— | 8 is more than 5 so round up. |

**b** 48.456 ...............

**c** 30.303 ...............

**d** 8.997 ...............

> To round to 2 decimal places (2 d.p.), look at the digit in the third decimal place.

**5** Use a calculator to write these fractions as decimals correct to 2 decimal places.

**a** $\frac{1}{7}$ ...............  Work out 1 ÷ 7  **b** $\frac{1}{8}$ ...............  **c** $\frac{1}{9}$ ...............

**6** **Reasoning** Joanne says that 32.999 rounded to 2 decimal places is 33.

**a** Explain why Joanne is wrong.

**b** What is the correct answer? ...............

**7** **Finance** Chloe buys a pack of five batteries for £1.99. How much does each battery cost? Round your answer to the nearest penny.

**8** $\sqrt{15}$ = 3.872983346 Round this number to 3 decimal places. ...............

> To round a decimal to 3 decimal places, look at the digit in the fourth decimal place.

**9** **Problem-solving** Emma writes down an answer of 7.48 correct to 2 decimal places. Circle the two numbers which could have been her unrounded answer.

7.475        7.485        7.484        7.4727

**10** **Problem-solving** Write down a number with 3 decimal places that would round to

**a** 6 to the nearest whole number and 5.7 to the nearest tenth ...............

**b** 5.5 to the nearest tenth and 5.55 to the nearest hundredth. ...............

**Check**  Tick each box as your **confidence** in this topic improves.    **Need extra help?** Go to page 61 and tick the boxes next to Q1 and 2. Then try them once you've finished 6.1–6.8.

53

**1** Find

  **a** 4525 × 0.01 ..................

  **b** 22.4 × 0.01 ..................

  **c** 777 × 0.01 ..................

**2** Find

  **a** 37 ÷ 0.1 ..................

  **b** 234 ÷ 0.001 ..................

  **c** 6.2 ÷ 0.01 ..................

**3** Find

  **a** 4.3 × 2.6

  **b** 6.5 × 3.8

  **c** 5.29 × 4.3

> **Guided**

Estimate: 4 × 3 = ...........

```
     4 3
  ×  2 6
  -------
   2 5 8
 + 8 6 0
  -------
 1 1 1 8
     1
```

Use a standard method to work out 43 × 26.

Use your estimate to see where to put the decimal point.

43 × 26 = 1118

so 4.3 × 2.6 = ...........

**Worked example**

**4** Evaluate these using a written method. Give your answers to 1 decimal place where appropriate.

To divide by a decimal, multiply both numbers by a power of 10 (10, 100, …) until you have a whole number to divide by. Then work out the division.

> **Guided**

  **a** 19.8 ÷ 1.5

$$\times 10 \left( \begin{array}{c} 1.5)\overline{19.8} \\ \\ 15)\overline{198} \end{array} \right) \times 10$$

1.5 has one decimal place, so multiply both numbers by 10.

  **b** 27.6 ÷ 0.92

0.92 has two decimal places, so multiply by 100.

**Worked example**

```
      1 3.......
15)1 9⁴8.³0
```

Work out the division.

Check: 15 × 13. .......... is between 10 × 13 = 130 and 20 × 13 = 260 ✓

**5** **Problem-solving** A factory makes 3.5 door frames every second.

  **a** Each door frame uses 4.9 m of wood. How many kilometres of wood are used every minute?

  **b** Each door frame is tied with two plastic ties. Each tie is 0.45 m long. A builder orders 125 door frames. What length of plastic ties are needed?

**Check** Tick each box as your **confidence** in this topic improves.

**Need extra help?** Go to page 61 and tick the boxes next to Q3 and 4. Then try them once you've finished 6.1–6.8.

54

1 Use a written method to convert these fractions to decimals.

   **a** $\frac{6}{10}$ ..................................... **b** $\frac{7}{8}$ ..................................... **c** $\frac{17}{20}$ .....................................

2 **a** **Reasoning** Convert $\frac{1}{9}$ and $\frac{2}{9}$ into decimals.

   **b** Use your answers to part a to write the values of $\frac{3}{9}, \frac{4}{9}, \frac{5}{9}, \frac{6}{9}, \frac{7}{9}, \frac{8}{9}$.

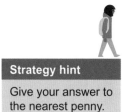

3 **Finance** On one day £22 is worth $37. How much is $1 worth?

4 Write these recurring decimals as fractions.

**Guided**

   **a** $0.\dot{5}$

$$0.\dot{5} = 0.5555555... = n$$
$$10n = ..................$$
$$10n - n = .............. - ..............$$
$$9n = ..................$$
$$n = ..................$$

   | Call the decimal $n$. |

   | Multiply the decimal by 10. |

   | Subtract the value of $n$ from the value of $10n$ so you get all the decimal places to zero. |

   | Solve the equation. |

   **b** $0.\dot{8}$

5 Write these recurring decimals as fractions.

   **a** $0.\dot{2}\dot{9}$

   **b** $0.\dot{3}1\dot{8}$

   **c** $0.\dot{5}7\dot{4}$

6 Write these recurring decimals as fractions.

   **a** $0.1\dot{3}$

   **b** $0.5\dot{7}$

7 Change these recurring decimals into mixed numbers.

   **a** $5.\dot{2}$

   **b** $4.\dot{1}\dot{8}$

**Check** Tick each box as your **confidence** in this topic improves.  **Need extra help?** Go to page 61 and tick the boxes next to Q5 and 6. Then try them once you've finished 6.1–6.8.

55

**1** Work out

  **a** $\frac{3}{7}$ of 21 cm ......................................

  **b** $\frac{5}{6}$ of 18 kg ......................................

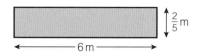
In maths, $\frac{3}{4}$ of 100 is the same as $\frac{3}{4} \times 100$.

**2** Work out the area of this rectangle. Simplify your answer.

$\frac{2}{5}$ m

6 m

**3** Work out these multiplications. Use the fraction wall to check your answer.

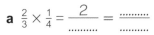

  **a** $\frac{2}{3} \times \frac{1}{4} = \frac{2}{\dots} = \frac{\dots}{\dots}$

  **b** $\frac{1}{3} \times \frac{1}{2}$ ......................................

  **c** $-\frac{1}{4} \times \frac{2}{3}$ ......................................

To multiply two fractions, multiply their numerators and multiply their denominators.

Use the rule for multiplying negative numbers.

**4** Look at this square.

  **a** Work out the perimeter. ......................................

  **b** Work out the area. ......................................

$\frac{5}{8}$ m

**5** Work out

  **a** $\frac{4}{5} \times \frac{15}{22} = \frac{4}{_{1}\cancel{5}} \times \frac{\cancel{15}^{3}}{22}$ ⟶ 5 goes into 5 once, 5 goes into 15 three times

  $= \frac{^{2}\cancel{4}}{5} \times \frac{3}{\cancel{22}_{11}}$ ⟶ 2 goes into 4 twice, 2 goes into 22 eleven times

  $= \frac{2}{1} \times \frac{3}{11} = \frac{6}{\dots}$

**Worked example**

  **b** $\frac{9}{10} \times \frac{35}{36}$

  **c** $\frac{16}{25} \times \frac{5}{32}$

  **d** $\frac{6}{13} \times \frac{5}{9} \times \frac{13}{20}$

  **e** $\frac{7}{9} \times \frac{2}{39} \times \frac{13}{14}$

**Check** Tick each box as your **confidence** in this topic improves.

😟 😐 😊

**Need extra help?** Go to page 62 and tick the boxes next to Q7 and 8. Then try them once you've finished 6.1–6.8.

56

**1** Write down the reciprocal of

**a** $\frac{3}{4}$ .................

**b** 6 .................

**c** $\frac{1}{8}$ .................

**d** 9 .................

The **reciprocal** of a fraction is the 'upside down' or inverse of that fraction.

The reciprocal of $\frac{2}{5}$ is $\frac{5}{2}$

$6 = \frac{6}{1}$

**2** Write down the reciprocal of

**a** $3\frac{1}{2}$ .................

**b** $1\frac{1}{3}$ .................

**c** $4\frac{3}{5}$ .................

**d** $2\frac{5}{7}$ .................

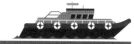

**Strategy hint**

Write mixed numbers as improper fractions first.

**3** Use the reciprocal to work out

**Guided**

**a** $2 \div \frac{1}{5}$

$= 2 \times \frac{5}{1}$ ← The reciprocal of $\frac{1}{5}$ is $\frac{5}{1}$

$= \frac{2}{1} \times \frac{5}{1}$

$= 10$

**b** $4 \div \frac{4}{7}$

To divide by a fraction, multiply by the reciprocal.

**c** $10 \div \frac{15}{16}$

**d** $7 \div \frac{2}{3}$

**e** $\frac{1}{5} \div \frac{4}{9}$

**4** Use the reciprocal to work out

**Guided**

**a** $\frac{2}{3} \div \frac{2}{7}$

$= \frac{2}{3} \times \frac{7}{2}$ ← The reciprocal of $\frac{2}{7}$ is $\frac{7}{2}$

$= \frac{14}{6} = \frac{7}{3}$

**b** $\frac{5}{9} \div \frac{2}{3}$

**c** $\frac{5}{11} \div \frac{12}{13}$

**5** A large sack of sugar contains $10\frac{1}{2}$ kg.

How many $\frac{2}{5}$ kg bags can be filled from the large bag?

**6** A large loaf of bread is $10\frac{2}{3}$ inches long.

**a** How many slices of bread can be cut from the large loaf if each slice is to be three-quarters of an inch thick?

**b** How long is the piece of bread that is left over?

**Check** Tick each box as your **confidence** in this topic improves.

 ☹ 😐 ☺

**Need extra help?** Go to page 62 and tick the box next to Q9. Then try it once you've finished 6.1–6.8.

57

**Guided**

**1** Work out $\frac{1}{2} + \frac{2}{5}$

$$\frac{1}{2} + \frac{2}{5} = \frac{5}{10} + \frac{\dots}{10}$$

$$= \frac{\dots}{10}$$

To add or subtract fractions write them as equivalent fractions with the same denominator. Use the LCM as the denominator.

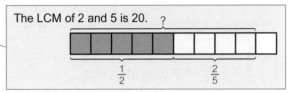

The LCM of 2 and 5 is 20.

**2** Work out

**a** $\frac{1}{3} + \frac{2}{5}$ .......................................

**b** $\frac{3}{4} - \frac{1}{3}$ .......................................

**3** **Reasoning** Vikram says, '$\frac{1}{3} + \frac{1}{2} = \frac{2}{5}$'

**a** Use these bars to explain what mistake she has made.

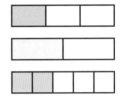

**b** Work out $\frac{1}{3} + \frac{1}{2}$ by writing both fractions with denominator 6. .......................................

**4** Work out

**a** $\frac{1}{3} + \frac{1}{7}$ .......................................  **b** $\frac{3}{4} - \frac{2}{5}$ .......................................

**5** Work out each of these. Give each answer in its simplest form, and as a mixed number where necessary.

**a** $\frac{1}{2} + \frac{2}{3} + \frac{3}{4}$ .......................................

**b** $\frac{21}{4} - \frac{17}{6}$ .......................................

**6** Ume adds two mixed numbers with different denominators to get $4\frac{1}{4}$.

What two numbers might he have added?

**Strategy hint**

Start with a mixed number with some quarters.

**Check**  Tick each box as your **confidence** in this topic improves.

**Need extra help?** Go to page 62 and tick the boxes next to Q10 and 11. Then try them once you've finished 6.1–6.8.

**Guided**

1 Write these mixed numbers as improper fractions.

   **a** $3\frac{2}{5} = \frac{15}{5} + \frac{2}{5} = $ ............

   **b** $5\frac{1}{4}$ ................................................

**Guided**

2 Work out these calculations of mixed numbers. Write the answers in their simplest form.

   **a** $4\frac{1}{2} + 3\frac{1}{4} = 7 + \frac{2}{4} + \frac{1}{4} = $ .................

   **b** $1\frac{3}{4} + 4\frac{3}{5}$ ........................................................

   **c** $5\frac{5}{6} - 2\frac{1}{3}$ ................................

   **d** $4\frac{1}{6} + 2\frac{1}{10}$ ......................................

3 **Real / Problem-solving** Mai is travelling from Perth to Adelaide in Australia.

   **a** She spends $3\frac{1}{2}$ hours on the plane. She then travels for $1\frac{3}{4}$ hours by bus.
      How long does she spend travelling?

      ...........................................................................................

   **b** Mai sets off at 12:45. The time in Perth is $2\frac{1}{2}$ hours behind Adelaide.
      At what time does she arrive in Adelaide? ................................

**Guided**

4 Work out these subtractions.

   **a** $3\frac{3}{5} - 2\frac{1}{10} = \dfrac{18}{5} - \dfrac{21}{10}$  —  Write both numbers as improper fractions.

            $= \dfrac{36}{10} - \dfrac{21}{10}$  —  Write the fractions with a common denominator.

            $= \dfrac{\text{.........}}{10} = $ .............  —  Write the answer as a mixed number.

   **b** $3\frac{1}{4} - 1\frac{2}{3}$

> It is usually easier to write mixed numbers as improper fractions before doing the calculation.

5 Work out

   **a** $3\frac{1}{3} \times 4\,\text{cm}$ ...........................................................

   **b** $2\frac{4}{5} \times 2\frac{3}{4}$ ..........................................................

> Write mixed numbers as improper fractions before multiplying.

6 Work out

   **a** $3\frac{1}{4} \div 2$ ...........................................................

   **b** $2\frac{4}{5} \div 3$ ...........................................................

   **c** $3\frac{1}{4} \div \frac{4}{5}$ ...........................................................

**Worked example**

7 Find the length of this rectangle.

> Area $= 4\frac{2}{5}$ m²    $\frac{5}{6}$ m

**Check**    Tick each box as your **confidence** in this topic improves.    ☹ 😐 ☺    **Need extra help?** Go to page 62 and tick the box next to Q12. Then try it once you've finished 6.1–6.8.

59

**1 STEM** The minimum thickness of a circuit board is 0.2 mm.

Write down how many of these circuit boards have the same thickness as

**a** a 1.6 mm thick circuit board

$1.6 \div 0.2 =$

Multiply both sides by 10.

$16 \div 2 = \ldots\ldots\ldots$

**b** a 2.8 mm thick circuit board.

**2 Problem-solving**

**a** A car travels 1.8 km every minute.

How many kilometres does it travel in two and a half hours?

**b** If the car travels at constant speed, how long will it take it to travel 540 km?

**3 Real** Three bricks have thicknesses of $10\frac{1}{2}$ cm, $12\frac{1}{3}$ cm and 9.75 cm, respectively.

The bricks are placed on top of each other. Find the total thickness of the three bricks. Give your answer as a mixed number.

**4 Reasoning** A square sheet of metal of side length 23.8 cm has a rectangle with dimensions 8.4 cm by 4.2 cm cut from it. Find the area of metal that remains.

**5 Problem-solving** A bag of potatoes weighs 12.5 kg. Darius takes $\frac{3}{5}$ of the potatoes. Jasmine then takes $\frac{7}{10}$ of what is left in the original bag. What mass of potatoes does Jasmine take?

**6 Problem-solving** At a party there are three pizzas. Jo eats $\frac{3}{4}$ of a pizza, Ruairi eats $1\frac{1}{5}$ of a pizza and Jaime eats $\frac{2}{3}$ of a pizza. How much pizza is left? Give your answer as a fraction.

**Check**   Tick each box as your **confidence** in this topic improves.   ☹ ☺ ☺   **Need extra help?** Go to page 62 and tick the box next to Q13. Then try it once you've finished 6.1–6.8.

60

## Rounding decimals

1 Round each number to 2 decimal places.

a 0.752 .................

b 0.768 .................

c 0.7455 .................

d 0.7549 .................

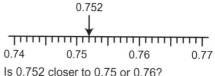

Use the number line to help you.

0.752

Is 0.752 closer to 0.75 or 0.76?

2 How much, to the nearest penny, is £4.30 ÷ 3? .................

£ ☐.☐☐

## Multiplying and dividing decimals

3 Use a written method to calculate

a $3.14 \times 2.7$

b $3.9 \times 8.62$

First estimate the answer.

4 Work out these divisions. Use a written method.
Give your answers to 1 decimal place where appropriate.

a $9.12 \div 1.2$

b $94.66 \div 2.5$

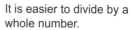

It is easier to divide by a whole number.

$$\times 10 \left( \begin{array}{c} 9.12 \div 1.2 \\ 91.2 \div 12 \end{array} \right) \times 10$$

## Converting fractions to decimals

5 Write these decimals with repeating digits as fractions.

a $0.\dot{5}\dot{3}$

b $0.\dot{2}\dot{8}$

c $0.3\dot{5}$

$$n = 0.5353\ldots$$

$$100n = 53.5353\ldots$$

$$100n - n = 53.5353\ldots$$

$$- \quad 0.5353\ldots$$

$$99n = \ldots\ldots\ldots$$

$$n = \ldots\ldots\ldots$$

6 Write these decimals with repeating digits as fractions.

a $0.4\dot{7}$

b $0.2\dot{4}$

c $0.1\dot{9}$

$$n = 0.4777\ldots$$

$$10n = 4.7777\ldots$$

$$100n = 47.777\ldots$$

$$100n - 10n = 47.777\ldots$$

$$- \quad 4.777\ldots$$

$$90n = \ldots\ldots\ldots$$

$$n = \ldots\ldots\ldots$$

## Multiplying fractions

**7** Find

**a** $6 \times \frac{1}{5} = 6$ lots of $\frac{1}{5} = \frac{1}{5} + \frac{1}{5} + \frac{1}{5} + \frac{1}{5} + \frac{1}{5} + \frac{1}{5} = \frac{\text{......}}{5} = \text{.....} \frac{\text{......}}{5}$

**b** $3 \times \frac{1}{6}$ ...............................................

**c** $\frac{3}{4} \times 5 = 5 \times \frac{3}{4} = $ ...................................................

**8** Work out these multiplications. Simplify the fractions first.

**a** $\frac{5}{8} \times \frac{4}{5} = \frac{5 \times 4}{8 \times 5} = \frac{\cancel{4} \times 5}{\cancel{8} \times 5} = \frac{\text{..........}}{\text{..........}} \times \frac{\text{..........}}{\text{..........}} = \frac{\text{..........}}{\text{..........}}$

**b** $\frac{8}{33} \times \frac{11}{12}$ ...................................................

## Dividing by fractions

**9** Work out

**a** $\frac{1}{2} \div \frac{2}{5} = \frac{1}{2} \times \frac{\text{......}}{2} = \frac{\text{......}}{4}$    **b** $\frac{2}{3} \div \frac{5}{7}$ ....................

> **Strategy hint**
>
> Multiply the first number by the reciprocal of the second.

## Adding and subtracting fractions

**10** Complete the following

**a** The lowest common multiple of 5 and 4 is 20

$\frac{3}{5} + \frac{1}{4} = \frac{\text{......}}{20} + \frac{\text{......}}{20} = \frac{\text{......}}{20}$

**b** The lowest common multiple of 3 and 8 is ..................

$\frac{1}{3} + \frac{3}{8} = \frac{\text{..........}}{\text{..........}} + \frac{\text{..........}}{\text{..........}} = \frac{\text{..........}}{\text{..........}}$

**11** Work out

**a** $\frac{4}{5} + \frac{1}{9}$ ...........................................    **b** $\frac{3}{5} - \frac{4}{11}$ ...........................................

## Calculating with mixed numbers

**12** Work out these mixed number calculations.

**a** $1\frac{1}{3} + 2\frac{1}{3} = 1 + 2 + \frac{1}{3} + \frac{1}{3} = $ ..................

**b** $3\frac{2}{5} + 5\frac{3}{5}$ ........................................................

**c** $6 - 2\frac{1}{2} = \frac{12}{2} - $ .............................................

Write as halves:

12 halves $- \square$ halves $= \square$ halves

**d** $4\frac{4}{5} - 2\frac{1}{5}$ .............................................................

**e** $3\frac{1}{2} \div \frac{1}{4}$ .............................................................

**f** $\frac{5}{6} \times 2\frac{1}{5}$ .............................................................

Dividing by a fraction is the same as multiplying by its reciprocal. Write mixed numbers as improper fractions. Give your answer as mixed numbers.

## Solving problems with fractions and decimals

**13** **Challenge** Three students share $37.50. Leena gets 0.35 of the total, Shika gets $\frac{1}{3}$ and Jing gets what is left. How much does each student get? Give your answer to the nearest cent.

1 **Problem-solving** Sami rounded a number with 3 decimal places to 2 decimal places and got the answer 34.67.

    **a** What is the smallest number Sami could have rounded up to 34.67? .................

    **b** What is the largest number Sami could have rounded down to 34.67? .................

 2 **Reasoning**

    **a** A cuboid-shaped box has dimensions 13.2 cm by 8.8 cm by 4.5 cm.

    What is the volume of the box? .................................................................................

    **b** Another box has dimensions 1.1 cm by 2.2 cm by 0.9 cm.

    How many of these boxes will fit in the first box?

 3 **Real** A skyscraper is 361.9 m high. The height of each floor is 3.85 m. How many floors high is the skyscraper?

...................................................................................................................................

 4 Find the decimal equivalent of all the fractions less than 1 with the denominator 7.
What do you notice about this set of decimals?

Look at the recurring digits in the answers.

5 Write these decimals with repeating digits as fractions.

    **a** 0.37̇1̇                **b** 0.92̇7̇

You might need to form equations for 10, 100 or 1000 × the decimal.

6 Work out

    **a** $\frac{18}{37} + \frac{3}{10}$             **b** $\frac{17}{20} - \frac{5}{23}$

**Worked example**

7 How many 0.4 litre water bottles can be filled from a 55.2 litre bottle of water?

8 Complete this magic square so that each row, column and diagonal sums to the same number.

| $\frac{1}{2}$ | | |
| $2\frac{2}{3}$ | | |
| $1\frac{1}{3}$ | | $2\frac{1}{2}$ |

9 **Reasoning** Mehmet shares $128.44 between his brother and sister. He gives his brother $\frac{9}{20}$ of the amount and the rest to his sister.
How much do they each receive? Give your answers to the nearest cent.

10 **Reasoning** A rectangular piece of cardboard measures $12\frac{3}{4}$ inches by $8\frac{1}{3}$ inches.
A small rectangle measuring $2\frac{5}{6}$ inches by $3\frac{1}{4}$ inches is cut from it.
What area of cardboard is left after the small rectangle has been removed?
Give your answer to the nearest whole number.

11 **Reasoning** A ski shop owner calculates that $\frac{3}{4}$ of her customers rent skis.
Half of the people who rent skis also rent crash helmets.

How many crash helmets does she expect to rent from 80 customers?

12 **STEM / Problem-solving** A cube of copper has a side length of $\frac{1}{20}$ m.

a Work out the volume of the copper cube.

The copper is shaped into a square with an area of $\frac{1}{16}$ m$^2$.

Volume of a cuboid
= length × width × height

b Work out the side length of the copper square.

The copper square is $\frac{1}{500}$ m thick.

c Show that the volume of copper has remained unchanged.

1 Round 3.56894 to

  **a** 2 decimal places ........................    **b** 3 decimal places. ........................

2 Use a written method to calculate $2.3 \times 6.85$.

3 Work out

  **a** $\frac{2}{3} \times \frac{5}{8}$ ................................................................................................................

  **b** $\frac{3}{5} \times -\frac{3}{4}$ ................................................................................................................

4 Evaluate

  **a** $\frac{4}{5} \div \frac{3}{4}$ ................................................................................................................

  **b** $-\frac{5}{7} \div -\frac{10}{11}$ ................................................................................................................

5 Write $\frac{5}{9}$ as a decimal using dot notation.

6 Find

  **a** $5\frac{1}{12} + 2\frac{6}{11}$

  **b** $12\frac{2}{3} - 12\frac{3}{5}$

7 Write $3.\dot{5}0\dot{4}$ as a fraction.

**1 STEM** A sports club changed the training programme for its athletes. After the first year, the athletes were asked how they felt about the new training. The results are shown in the frequency table.

| Outcome | Frequency | Experimental probability |
|---|---|---|
| very happy | 60 | |
| fairly happy | 20 | |
| not happy or no improvement | 10 | |
| **Total frequency** | | |

Experimental probability for 'very happy'

$= \dfrac{\text{number of athletes who were 'very happy'}}{\text{total number of athletes}}$

$= \dfrac{60}{\square}$

**a** Work out the total frequency. Write this in the table.
Total frequency is 60 + 20 + ......... = .........

**b** Calculate the experimental probability of each outcome and complete the table.

**c** The sports club claims that athletes using the new training programme are very likely to be happy with the results. Comment on this claim.

**2 Real** A manufacturer tested a new kind of electric car. They claim that there is a 90% experimental probability that the car will travel at least 150 miles on one charge.

**a** Can you tell from the probability how many electric cars they tested? .........................................

**b** What would make you confident that their claim was correct?

The more times an experiment is repeated, the more reliable the estimated probability.

**3 Real / Modelling** Records show that in Cyprus it was sunny on 888 days out of the last 1000 days.

**a** Estimate the probability that it will be sunny in Cyprus tomorrow.

**b** Is this a good model for predicting the weather in Cyprus for Christmas Day? Give a reason for your answer.

Worked example

**4 Problem-solving** The records of a car showroom show that 8 out of the last 25 customers paid for alloy wheels as an extra, and 11 paid for metallic paint as an extra.

**a** Estimate the probability that the next customer pays for

**i** alloy wheels as an extra .........................

**ii** metallic paint as an extra. .......................

**b** A car salesman worked out 8 + 11 = 19 and estimated that the probability of a customer paying for alloy wheels or metallic paint as an extra is $\frac{19}{25}$. Explain why he might be wrong.

What would the salesman have estimated if 15 had paid for alloy wheels and 20 had paid for metallic paint?

**Check** Tick each box as your **confidence** in this topic improves.

**Need extra help?** Go to page 68 and tick the boxes next to Q1–3. Then try them once you've finished 7.1–7.2.

66

**1 Real / Reasoning** The table shows how many goals England scored in each match they played from September 2007 to their World Cup exit in 2014.

a Complete the table.

> For a set of data, the relative frequency
> of a value = $\frac{\text{frequency of value}}{\text{total frequency}}$

| Goals | Frequency | Relative frequency |
|-------|-----------|--------------------|
| 0 | 9 | $\frac{9}{80}$ |
| 1 | 22 | $\frac{22}{80}$ |
| 2 | 24 | |
| 3 | 13 | |
| 4 | 6 | |
| 5 | 4 | |
| 6 | 1 | |
| 7 | 0 | |
| 8 | 1 | |
| Total | 80 | |

Relative frequency can be used to estimate the probability of an event happening.

> You can expect $\frac{\square}{80}$ of the 400
> matches to have 3 goals scored.

> Add all the frequencies to find the total.

b Estimate the probability that England will score 2 goals in their next match. ...............

c England played 400 matches from September 1979 to 2014.
  In how many of these matches would you expect 3 goals to have been scored?

**2** A dentist's records show that 11 of the last 50 patients had a tooth filling and 7 of them had an X-ray.

a Estimate the probability that the next patient has

  i  a tooth filling ...............    ii  an X-ray. ...............

b Of the next 300 patients, how many would you expect to have an X-ray?

> Probability can be used to model what happens in the future.

c Is the probability of a patient having a tooth filling and an X-ray equal to $\frac{11}{50} + \frac{7}{50} = \frac{18}{50}$? Explain.

**3 Problem-solving / Reasoning**

a Ellie asked 20 football fans which team they support. Seven said Stoke City. Estimate the probability that a fan supports Stoke City. ...............

b Adam asked 80 football fans which team they support. 35 said Stoke City. Estimate the probability that a fan supports Stoke City. ...............

> The more data you have, the more confident you can be about any conclusions based on the data.

c Which estimate do you think is more reliable? Give a reason for your answer.

d Ellie and Adam shared their data.

  i  Use their combined data to estimate the probability that a football fan supports Stoke City.

  ii  They interview another 200 fans. How many would you expect to support Stoke City?

**Check**  Tick each box as your **confidence** in this topic improves.    **Need extra help?** Go to page 69 and tick the boxes next to Q4–6. Then try them once you've finished 7.1–7.2.

67

## Experimental probability

1 A group of students spin a four-coloured spinner repeatedly for an hour.
The tally chart shows the results.

| Colour | Tally | Frequency | Experimental probability |
|--------|-------|-----------|--------------------------|
| gold | 卌 II | 7 | $\dfrac{7}{\square}$ |
| silver | 卌 卌 III | 13 | |
| purple | 卌 卌 卌 I | | |
| red | 卌 卌 IIII | | |
| **Total frequency** | | | |

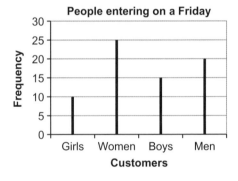

Write each frequency as a fraction with the total frequency as the denominator.
The spinner landed on gold 7 times.

**a i** Complete the Frequency column.     **ii** Calculate and write the total frequency.

**b** Complete the table by calculating the experimental probability for each colour.

**c** How many times would you expect the spinner to land on gold in 100 spins? ........................

2 The bar-line chart shows the people entering a supermarket in one minute on a Friday morning.

**a** How many people entered the supermarket during that time?

**b** Estimate the probability that the next person entering on Friday morning will be a boy.

**People entering on a Friday**

Frequency / Customers: Girls 10, Women 25, Boys 15, Men 20

**c Reasoning** Is your answer to part **b** a good estimate for the probability that the next person entering the supermarket late on a Friday night will be a boy?
Give a reason for your answer.

Would children go shopping late on a Friday night?

3 The scores that a snooker player gets in a tournament are shown in the table.

| Score | 1–30 | 31–60 | 61–90 | 91–120 | 121–150 |
|-------|------|-------|-------|--------|---------|
| Frequency | 18 | 35 | 21 | 8 | 2 |

Estimate the probability that his next score is

**a** more than 90 ........................

**b** less than 60. ........................

## Estimating probability

4 A veterinary surgery records the first 20 pets that arrive for treatment.
They record the frequencies in a table.

| Pet | Frequency | Relative frequency |
|---|---|---|
| Cat | 11 | $\frac{11}{20}$ |
| Parrot | 7 | $\frac{........}{20}$ |
| Other | 2 | $\frac{........}{20}$ |
| **Total frequency** | 20 | |

a Estimate the probability that the next pet to need treatment is a cat. ........................

b Estimate the probabilities for parrot and for other.

c The surgery recorded the next 80 pets to arrive for treatment.
Write down how many pets you would expect to be

> Use the relative frequency as the estimate of probability.

**Guided**

i cats

$$\frac{11}{20} \text{ of } 80 = \frac{11}{20} \times 80 = ........................$$

ii parrots

iii other

5 Fastfit keeps records of all the repairs it makes to motorcycles.

The table shows the information about all the repairs made in 2018.

| Cost (£$C$) | Frequency |
|---|---|
| $0 < C \leqslant 200$ | 36 |
| $200 < C \leqslant 400$ | 45 |
| $400 < C \leqslant 600$ | 18 |
| $600 < C \leqslant 800$ | 21 |
| $800 < C \leqslant 1000$ | 8 |

a Persa needs to repair her motorcycle.

Estimate the probability that the repair will cost

i more than £400 ..............      ii between £200 and £600. ...................

b Comment on the accuracy of your estimate.

.................................................................................................................................

6 An electrical supplier notices that 6 out of every 100 toasters that he sells are faulty.

a Estimate the probability that the next toaster he supplies is faulty.

.................................................................................................................................

b The electrical supplier sold 450 toasters in 2018.
How many would you expect to have been faulty?

.................................................................................................................................

**1** The table shows the number of balls potted (hit a ball into a hole) by two pool players on each visit to the table.

| Balls potted | 0 | 1 | 2 | 3 | 4 | 5 | 6 | 7 | 8 |
|---|---|---|---|---|---|---|---|---|---|
| Player A | 2 | 5 | 12 | 16 | 28 | 30 | 18 | 14 | 4 |
| Player B | 4 | 8 | 15 | 26 | 26 | 17 | 12 | 8 | 1 |

**a** Estimate the probability that

  **i** player A pots 4 balls

  **ii** player B pots 4 balls.

**b** Which player is more likely to pot 7 balls? Explain your answer.

**c** **Modelling** Whose estimated probability is a more reliable model for their future visits to the table? Explain your answer.

**d** Player A visits the table 150 times.

Estimate the number of times she pots 8 balls.

......................................................................................................................................................................

**2 Real** The lengths of carrots sold by a farmer are shown in the table.

| Length, $l$ (cm) | Frequency |
|---|---|
| $10 < l \leqslant 12$ | 20 |
| $12 < l \leqslant 14$ | 34 |
| $14 < l \leqslant 16$ | 48 |
| $16 < l \leqslant 18$ | 51 |
| $18 < l \leqslant 20$ | 28 |

**a** Estimate the probability that a carrot chosen at random has a length of 14 cm or less.

...............................................................................................

**b** In a sample of 1000 carrots, how many would you expect to measure between 18 cm and 20 cm?

......................................................................................................................................................................

**3 STEM** The iron levels found in blood samples of some adult men are shown in the table.

| Iron level, $m$ (µg/d$l$) | Frequency |
|---|---|
| $0 \leqslant m < 25$ | 15 |
| $25 \leqslant m < 50$ | 18 |
| $50 \leqslant m < 75$ | 46 |
| $75 \leqslant m < 100$ | 85 |
| $100 \leqslant m < 125$ | 72 |
| $125 \leqslant m < 150$ | 60 |
| $150 \leqslant m < 175$ | 42 |
| $175 \leqslant m < 200$ | 14 |

**a** Estimate the probability that a blood sample chosen at random contains less than 100 µg/d$l$ of iron.

...............................................................................................

**b** Dave thinks that the normal range for iron levels in adult men is 50 µg/d$l \leqslant m < 175$ µg/d$l$.
Does the data support his belief?

**c** Investigate the normal range for iron levels in adult men. Was Dave correct?

**4 STEM / Reasoning** The probability that a ball bearing is faulty is 0.0001 when the production process is working properly. A testing machine found that three ball bearing were faulty out of a batch of 10 000. Is the production process working properly? Explain your answer.

**5** You need a coin. Use a piece of removable adhesive or sticky tape to stick a small item such as a paper clip to one side of the coin.

**a** Flip the coin 20 times. Record the results in the tally chart.

| Outcome | Tally | Frequency |
|---|---|---|
| heads | | |
| tails | | |
| Total frequency | | |

**b** Work out the experimental probability of heads. .........................

**c i** Repeat the experiment by flipping the coin 30 times and complete the tally chart.

| Outcome | Tally | Frequency |
|---|---|---|
| heads | | |
| tails | | |
| Total frequency | | |

Compare the probabilities as decimals, as percentages or as fractions with the same denominator.

**ii** Work out the experimental probability of heads. .........................

**iii** Compare this experimental probability with your answer in part **b**.

**d** Calculate the experimental probabilities for the combined data from your two experiments.

**e i** If you flipped your coin 200 times, how many times would you expect to get heads?

**ii** Do you think this is more or less frequent than if you had used a fair coin? Explain your answer.

**6 Problem-solving** Some traffic lights on Bill's journey to work have been set with these durations in seconds.

Work out the probability that the traffic lights are green when Bill first sees them in the morning.
Write your answer as a percentage.

| Colour setting | Duration (s) |
|---|---|
| red | 50 |
| red and amber | 5 |
| green | 40 |
| amber | 5 |

**Strategy hint**

Work out the total duration of the traffic light colours.

1 **STEM / Reasoning** A biologist records the number of each specimen she finds in a pond dipping experiment. She recorded her results in a frequency table.

| Specimen | Frequency |
|---|---|
| tadpole | 146 |
| pondskater | 38 |
| newtpole | 16 |
| **Total frequency** | |

Draw a column for experimental probability and write your answers clearly as fractions, $\frac{\square}{\square}$.

a Work out the experimental probability of each specimen.

b The biologist concludes that finding a newtpole in a pond is very unlikely.
Do you agree with this statement? Explain.

2 In a survey of runners after a 10 km race, 20% said they had achieved their target time and 5% said they achieved better than their target.

Another survey questions 300 athletes. How many would you expect to achieve their target time or better? ......................

3 Erin records the number of siblings each student has as 50 students arrive at school.

a Work out the experimental probability of each number of siblings.

b Erin says that it is unlikely that the next student to arrive at school will have 2 siblings. Do you agree? Explain.

c How could Erin get more accurate estimates of these probabilities?

| Number of siblings | Frequency |
|---|---|
| 0 | 18 |
| 1 | 16 |
| 2 | 12 |
| 3 | 3 |
| 4 | 1 |

4 A warehouse manager notices that 24 out of every 500 packages sent from the warehouse are reported as damaged when they arrive at their destination.

a Estimate the probability that a package will be reported as damaged. ......................

b The company distributed 11 600 packages in October 2018.

How many would you expect to have been reported as damaged? ......................

5 The average distance that 90 professional golfers drive (hit) the ball is shown in the table.

a A golfer is chosen at random. Estimate the probability that his average drive travels more than 175 m. ......................

b Rajan drives the ball an average distance of 225 m. He says that he can drive the ball further than 80% of the golfers whose data is recorded in the table. Is he correct?

| Distance, $d$ (m) | Frequency |
|---|---|
| $150 < d \leqslant 175$ | 18 |
| $175 < d \leqslant 200$ | 20 |
| $200 < d \leqslant 225$ | 24 |
| $225 < d \leqslant 250$ | 22 |
| $250 < d \leqslant 275$ | 6 |

**1** Write these percentages as fractions and as decimals.

  **a** $155\% = 1.55 = 1\frac{55}{100} = 1\frac{.....}{20}$

  **b** 115% ......................................................

  **c** 295% ...............................................

  **d** 345% .....................................................

**2** Complete this table.

| Mixed number | $1\frac{3}{20}$ | | | | |
|---|---|---|---|---|---|
| Decimal | | 1.65 | | | 3.15 |
| Percentage | | | 235% | 285% | |

A positive mixed number is greater than 1, so the decimal equivalent is greater than 1 and the percentage equivalent is greater than 100%.
For example, $1\frac{3}{4} = 1.75 = 175\%$.

**3** Write these percentages as decimals and fractions.

  **a** $124\% = 1.24 = 1\frac{24}{100} = 1\frac{.....}{25}$

  **b** 208% ...............................................

  **c** 232% ...............................................

  **d** 356% ...............................................

**4** Write these percentages as decimals and fractions.

  **a** $22.5\% = 22.5 \div 100 = 0.225$

$$= \frac{.............}{1000} \overset{\div 25}{\underset{\div 25}{\rightleftharpoons}} \frac{.....}{40}$$

Sometimes you might need to use a denominator of 1000 when you convert between fractions, decimals and percentages.

  **b** 2.5%

**5** Yasmin is comparing the satisfaction claims of two different websites.
Website A has 98% happy customers. Website B has 1404 happy customers out of 1440.
Which company has a higher proportion of happy customers?

**Check**    Tick each box as your **confidence** in this topic improves.    ☹ 😐 ☺    **Need extra help?** Go to page 79 and tick the boxes next to Q1–3. Then try them once you've finished 8.1–8.6.

73

**1** Rewrite these statements giving the proportions as percentages.

**a** 47 out of 50 students like baked beans. $\dfrac{47}{50} = \dfrac{94}{100} = 0.\ldots\ldots = \ldots\ldots\%$

> Write as a fraction. Change to a decimal, then to a percentage.

**b** 27 out of 90 students play football.

**c** 36 out of 45 students wish they had neater handwriting.

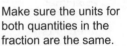

**2** A $\frac{1}{2}$ kg pot of fruit yogurt contains 30 g of sugar and 10 g of fat.

**a** What percentage of the yogurt is sugar? $\dfrac{30}{500} = \ldots\ldots\ldots\ldots\ldots\ldots\ldots\ldots$

> Make sure the units for both quantities in the fraction are the same.

**b** What percentage of the yogurt is fat? ...............................................

**3** Gina buys some cement. It costs £40 plus 20% VAT.

**a** Work out 20% of £40. $\dfrac{20}{100} \times 40 = \dfrac{800}{100} = £\ldots\ldots$

> To increase an amount by a percentage, you can find the percentage of the amount, then add it to the original amount.

**b** What is the total cost of the cement? £40 + £........ = £..........

**4** An MP3 player costs £35. It is reduced in a sale by 10%.

> To decrease an amount by a percentage, you can find the percentage of the amount, then subtract it from the original amount.

**a** Work out 10% of £35. ........................................................

**b** Work out the sale price of the MP3 player. ..........................................................

**Worked example**

**5** **Real** The Department of Education have a yearly budget of £46 500 million.
They have to decrease this budget by 8% for the next year. What is their new budget?

**6** **Problem-solving** Dan spends £805 on a holiday. His hotel normally costs £390 but there is a 20% discount. He spends £125 on travel and the rest on having fun.
How much does he spend on having fun?

**Check** Tick each box as your **confidence** in this topic improves.

**Need extra help?** Go to page 79 and tick the boxes next to Q4–5. Then try them once you've finished 8.1–8.6.

74

**1** An investor says, 'My investments have gone up by 150%.' She had invested £40 000. How much is her investment worth now?

**2** Ollie invests £4000. He earns 3% simple interest per year. How much interest does he earn in one year?

> Simple interest is the interest calculated only on the original amount of money invested. It is the same amount each year. Work out 3% of £4000.

**3** A phone costs £75. In a sale, the price of the phone is reduced by 70%.

  **a** Work out 70% of £75. ..............................................................................................................

  **b** Work out the sale price of the phone. ....................................................................................

  **c** Work out 30% of £75. ..............................................................................................................

  **d** What do you notice about your answers to parts **b** and **c**? Explain your answer.

**Guided**

**4** Work out these percentage increases and decreases. Use a decimal multiplier for each one.

  **a** Decrease 220 kg by 10%.

$$100\% - 10\% = 90\%$$
$$90\% = 0\ldots\ldots$$
$$220 \div 0.\ldots\ldots = \ldots\ldots$$

  **b** Increase 140 kg by 30%.

> 100% + 30% = □, so multiplier is □.

**5** **Finance** Sam invests £16 000 for 4 years at simple interest of 3.5%. How much is his investment worth at the end of the 4 years?

**6** Work out the original amount for each of these.

**Guided**

  **a** 20% of an amount is £60.

  ÷ 20 ( 20% = £60 ) ÷ 20
        1% = £3
  × 100 ( 100% = ............ ) × 100

  **b** 60% of an amount is 360 g.

> Sometimes you want to find the original amount after a percentage increase or decrease. You can use the unitary method.
>
> ÷ 140 ( 140% = 560 ) ÷ 140
>      1% = □

  **c** 140% of an amount is 560 cm.

**7** The cost of a baseball cap is reduced by 20%. It now costs £6.40. How much was it originally?

   100% − 20% = 80%

> **Worked example**

**Check**    Tick each box as your **confidence** in this topic improves.

**Need extra help?** Go to pages 79 and 80 and tick the boxes next to Q6–9. Then try them once you've finished 8.1–8.6.

75

**1 Finance** Two banks have very similar interest rates. Work out the difference in the final balances if you invest $4000 in both banks for 3 years.

In compound interest, the interest earned each year is added to money in the account and earns interest the next year.
Most interest rates are compound interest rates.

| Bank | Interest rate | Start balance | End of Year 1 balance | End of Year 2 balance | End of Year 3 balance |
|------|---------------|---------------|-----------------------|-----------------------|-----------------------|
| A | 1.35% | $4000 | | | |
| B | 1.4% | $4000 | | | |

**Worked example**

**2 Finance** Amy's salary will rise by 2.7% every year for the next 5 years.
Her starting salary is $22 500.
What will she earn in 5 years' time?

Amount = 22 500 × 1.027⁵

$$\frac{100 + 2.7}{100} = 1.027$$

= ............................ (to the nearest penny)

You can calculate an amount after $n$ years' compound interest using the formula
Amount = initial amount × $\left(\dfrac{100 + \text{interest rate}}{100}\right)^n$

**Guided**

**3 Finance** A store card company charges interest at 2.9% per month on any outstanding balance.
A balance of $750 is left unpaid.
What is the balance after

750 × ☐    1 month
750 × ☐²    2 months

**a** 1 month          **b** 4 months          **c** 1 year?

**4** Salim invests $10 000 in a savings account.

The bank pays 2.5% compound interest per year.

How much does Salim have after 6 years?

**5** Ayesha invests $3000 in a savings account.

The bank pays 10% compound interest per year.

How many years would it take for Ayesha to double her investment?

**Check** Tick each box as your **confidence** in this topic improves.

**Need extra help?** Go to page 80 and tick the boxes next to Q10 and 11. Then try them once you've finished 8.1–8.6.

76

**1** Simplify each ratio.

   **a** 3 : 12                 **b** 39 : 13

   **c** 5 : 25                 **d** 36 : 9

 **2** Simplify each ratio into a whole number ratio in its simplest form.

   **a** 20 : 17.5             **b** 12 : 25.25

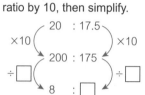

Simplify using powers of 10. 17.5 has one decimal place, so multiply both sides of the ratio by 10, then simplify.

**3** Fatima makes a hot drink by mixing 0.2 litres of coffee and 0.15 litres of hot chocolate.

   **a i** What percentage of the drink is coffee?

      **ii** What fraction of the drink is hot chocolate?

   **b** What is the ratio of coffee to chocolate in the drink?

**4** Write each ratio as a unit ratio. Give each answer to a maximum of 2 decimal places.

    **a** 11 : 5

Divide both sides of the ratio by the smaller number, 5.

You can compare ratios by writing them as unit ratios. In a unit ratio, one of the numbers is 1.

   **b** 11 : 8            **c** 7 : 22

**Worked example**

 **5 Real / STEM** Performance can be compared by looking at the ratio of power to weight.

   **a** Find the ratio of power to weight for each of these planes as a unit ratio.

| Plane | Power (kW) | Weight (kg) | Power : weight (unit ratio) |
|---|---|---|---|
| Wright flyer | 9 | 274 | 0.03 : 1 |
| Spitfire | 1096 | 2309 | |
| Concorde | 185 000 | 111 130 | |
| Boeing 747 | 245 000 | 178 100 | |
| F15 fighter jet | 109 000 | 18 200 | |

Use a calculator to work out $\frac{power}{weight}$ and round to 2 decimal places.

   **b** Which plane has the best performance? ...............................................

**Check**    Tick each box as your **confidence** in this topic improves.

**Need extra help?** Go to page 80 and tick the boxes next to Q13 and 15. Then try them once you've finished 8.1–8.6.

**Guided**

**1** Share $132 in the ratios given.

**a** 1 : 2 : 3

> How many parts there are in total?

1 + 2 + 3 = 6 parts

$132 ÷ 6 = $..............

> How much is each part worth?

1 part = 1 × $.............. = $..............

2 parts = 2 × $.............. = $..............

3 parts = 3 × $.............. = $..............

> Multiply the amount that one part is worth by each value in the ratio.

Check: ...............................................................

**b** 2 : 3 : 7

**2** A man decides to give $250 to his grandchildren aged 17, 13 and 10.
The children share the money in the same ratio as their ages.
How much does the youngest grandchild receive?

> **Strategy hint**
> Make sure both quantities are in the same units before working out the ratio.

**3** Write each ratio in its simplest form.

**a** 2 kg : 750 g

**b** 3 litres : 30 ml

**c** 450 mm : 0.9 m

**4** **Problem-solving** Rose gold can be made from a mix of gold, copper and silver in the ratio 150 : 44.5 : 5.5.

A rose gold bracelet has a mass of 80 g.
What are the masses of gold, copper and silver in the bracelet?

> Simplify the ratio into whole numbers. Then share the mass of the bracelet in the new ratio.

**5** **STEM** A type of stainless steel is made by mixing steel, chromium and nickel in the ratio 7.3 : 1.8 : 0.9.

| Mass | Steel | Chromium | Nickel |
|------|-------|----------|--------|
| 1 kg | | | |
| 2.5 kg | | | |

Complete the table to show how much of each metal is needed to make the quantities shown.

**6** **Reasoning** A paint machine makes green paint by mixing 1 litre of blue, 1.3 litres of yellow and 0.2 litres of red.
What proportion of the green paint is blue?

> First find the total volume of paint. Then write the proportion of blue as a fraction, and simplify.

**Check** Tick each box as your **confidence** in this topic improves.

☹ 😐 ☺

**Need extra help?** Go to page 80 and tick the boxes next to Q12 and 14. Then try them once you've finished 8.1–8.6.

78

## Fractions, decimals and percentages

1 Complete this table.

| Mixed number | $2\frac{1}{5}$ | | | $2\frac{1}{4}$ | | | $3\frac{4}{5}$ |
|---|---|---|---|---|---|---|---|
| Decimal | | | 4.2 | | 7.75 | | |
| Percentage | | 350% | | | | 530% | |

$1\frac{1}{5}$ = 1.2 and 120%, so $2\frac{1}{5}$ = 2.☐ and ☐%

2 Rewrite these statements giving the numbers as percentages.

a 7 out of 20 drinks are tea. ...............................................

b 22 out of 25 people are right handed. ...............................................

c 1 out of 5 cats preferred brand X. ...............................................

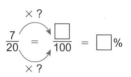

$$\frac{7}{20} \overset{\times\,?}{\underset{\times\,?}{=}} \frac{☐}{100} = ☐\%$$

3 Complete this table.

| Fraction in simplest terms | $\frac{31}{200}$ | $\frac{21}{500}$ | | | | |
|---|---|---|---|---|---|---|
| Fraction with denominator of 1000 | | | | | | |
| Decimal | | | 0.225 | 0.205 | | |
| Percentage | | | | | 17.5% | 87.5% |

Write each fraction with a denominator of 1000, then write as a decimal, then change to a percentage.
1000 ÷ 200 = 5,
so 200 × 5 = 1000

$$\frac{31}{200} \overset{\times\,5}{\underset{\times\,5}{=}} \frac{☐}{1000} = 0.155$$

0.155 × 100 = ☐%

## Using percentages

4 Increase these amounts by the given percentage.

a $40 by 20% ...............................................................................

b $20 by 15% ...............................................................................

Work out 10%. Double it to find 20%. Add it to $40.

5 Decrease these amounts by the given percentage.

a $40 by 5% ...............................................................................

b $60 by 30% ...............................................................................

6 **Finance** Piman invests $600 for 4 years at 3% simple interest per year. How much is his investment worth at the end of the 3 years?

Interest after 1 year = 3% of $600 = 0.03 × 600 = ...................

Interest after 4 years = 4 × ................... = ................... = ...................

Total value of investment = $600 + ................... = ...................

7 **Finance** Simone invests $800 for 4 years at 4.3% simple interest.

Work out how much her investment will be worth after 4 years.

Use the working in Q6 to help you.

**8** In a department store all prices have increased by 3%.
What was the original price of a pair of jeans that now costs $37.08?

$$\div 103 \left( \begin{array}{c} 103\% = \$37.08 \\ 1\% = \$0.36 \\ 100\% = \ldots\ldots\ldots \end{array} \right) \div 103$$
$$\times 100 \qquad \qquad \times 100$$

100% + 3% = 103%

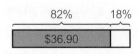

**9** In a sale the price of a pair of trainers has been reduced by 18% to $36.90.
Work out the original price before the sale.

$$\div 82 \left( \begin{array}{c} 82\% = \$36.90 \\ 1\% = \$0.45 \\ 100\% = \ldots\ldots\ldots \end{array} \right) \div 82$$
$$\times 100 \qquad \qquad \times 100$$

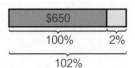

82%     18%

$36.90

**10** Samir invests $650 in the bank at 2% compound interest per year.
He leaves all the money in the bank.
Work out the amount at the end of 1 year, 2 years and 3 years.

$650 \times 1.02 = $ ............... end of year 1

............... $\times 1.02 = $ ............... end of year 2

............... $\times 1.02 = $ ............... end of year 3

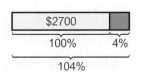

$650
100%     2%
102%

**11** Alina invests $2700 at 4% compound interest per year.
She leaves all the money in the bank.
How much will she have at the end of the third year?

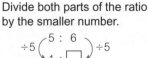

$2700
100%     4%
104%

## Ratio

**12** A ribbon is 2.5 m long. It is cut in the ratio 1 : 4.
How long will each piece be?

There are five parts.
2.5 ÷ 5 gives the
size of one part.

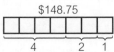

2.5 m

4     1

**13** Write each ratio as a unit ratio.

  **a** 5 : 6 ..............................

  **b** 2 : 3 ..............................

  **c** 9 : 4 ..............................

Divide both parts of the ratio
by the smaller number.

$$\div 5 \left( \begin{array}{c} 5 : 6 \\ 1 : \square \end{array} \right) \div 5$$

**14** Sal, Bob and Mick share $148.75 in the ratio 4 : 2 : 1.
How much did they each receive?

$148.75

4     2   1

**Worked
example**

**15** Simplify each ratio.

  **a** 5.5 : 4                    **b** 1.2 : 7.2

$$\times 2 \left( \begin{array}{c} 5.5 : 4 \\ 11 : \square \end{array} \right) \times 2$$

Choose a number to
multiply by that will
give a whole number.

**1 Finance** Josie invests $8000 for 4 years.

**a** Complete the table showing the value of her investment at the end of each year.

| Year | Value at start of year | Percentage change | Value at end of year |
|------|-----------------------|-------------------|----------------------|
| 1st | $8000 | 10% increase | $8800 |
| 2nd | $8800 | 10% increase | |
| 3rd | | 5% decrease | |
| 4th | | 3% increase | |

**b** Compare the value of her investment at the start of the 1st year and the end of the 4th year.

Work out

**i** the actual increase in her investment ........................

**ii** the percentage increase in her investment,
giving your answer correct to two decimal places.

Percentage increase

$$= \frac{\text{actual increase}}{\text{original amount}} \times 100$$

**2** Write these in ascending order.

$\frac{1}{22}$, $\frac{1}{4}$, 0.6, $\frac{3}{75}$, 2.2%, $\frac{2}{42}$

**3** A department store advertises a '20% off' day.
The next day prices return to normal.
A rival store says that the prices have gone up by 20% in a day

**a** Is the rival store right? ........................

**b** Explain your answer with an example.

**Strategy hint**

Choose a price and reduce it by 20%.

**4 STEM** The diameter of the Earth is 12756 km.
The table gives the diameters of four other planets in miles.

Write the ratio of the diameter of the Earth to the diameter of each planet in the form 1 : $n$.

| Planet | Diameter (miles) |
|--------|------------------|
| Mercury | 3031 |
| Venus | 7521 |
| Jupiter | 88846 |
| Saturn | 74900 |

12756 km ≈ .............. miles
 Earth : Mercury
 ........ : 3031
  1 : ........

Convert the radius of the Earth to miles so you only need to do one conversion.
8 km ≈ 5 miles

**5 Problem-solving** A shop sells newspapers, books and magazines in the ratio of 2 : 7 : 5.
In one week it sells 423 newspapers and books altogether. How many magazines does it sell?

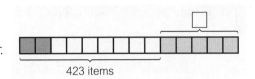

423 items

**6** A large cardboard box is 75 cm wide, 43 cm deep and 27.5 cm high.

**a** What is the volume of the box?

The large box contains smaller boxes.
All three dimensions of each small box are half of those of the large box.

**b** What is the volume of a small box?

**c** What is the ratio of the volume of the small box to the volume of the large box?

**d** How many small boxes can fit inside the large box?

**7 Reasoning** A car depreciates in value at a rate of approximately 15% per year.
At 2 years old it is worth £17 340.

**a** Work out the value of the car when it was

**i** 1 year old    **ii** new.

> **Literacy hint**
>
> Depreciates means goes down in value.

**b** Dom says, 'The car has depreciated 15% each year for 2 years, which makes 30% in total.

This means if I divide £17 340 by 0.7, I will find the value of the car when it is new.'
Is Dom correct? Explain your answer.

**8** In 2019 the world population was approximately 7.7 billion.

**a** What will the population be in 2030 if the population continues to increase at a rate of 1.1% per year?

**b** In what year will the world population reach 10 billion if the population continues to grow at the same rate?

1 Complete the table.

| Fraction or mixed number | $\frac{7}{10}$ | | | | | $1\frac{2}{5}$ |
|---|---|---|---|---|---|---|
| Decimal | | 0.25 | | | 2.5 | |
| Percentage | | | 160% | 75% | | |

2 Long lengths of rope need to be cut in the ratio 6 : 2 : 1.
How long is the longest piece cut from a 54 m length of rope?

3 Simplify each ratio.

   a 2.1 : 4.2                    b 3.3 : 5.5                    c 12 : 14.4

   ..................                   ..................                   ..................

4 5 miles is about the same as 8 km.
What is the ratio of miles to kilometres?
Give your answer in the form 1 : $n$.

5 A cricket bat costs $80. It is reduced in a sale by 15%.
Work out the sale price of the cricket bat.

6 20% of an amount is 4.2 g. Work out the original amount.

7 Alonso invests $4300 for 4 years at 4.3% simple interest per year.
How much is his investment worth after 4 years?

8 Rob invests $5450 in a savings account paying compound interest of 2% each year.
How much money will he have in his account after 4 years?

The properties of a shape are facts about its sides, angles, diagonals and symmetry.
Here are some of the properties of the special quadrilaterals that you should know.

| | | | |
|---|---|---|---|
| **Square**  | • all sides are equal in length<br>• opposite sides are parallel<br>• all angles are 90°<br>• diagonals bisect each other at 90° | **Rectangle** | • opposite sides are equal in length<br>• opposite sides are parallel<br>• all angles are 90°<br>• diagonals bisect each other |
| **Rhombus**  | • all sides are equal in length<br>• opposite sides are parallel<br>• opposite angles are equal<br>• diagonals bisect each other at 90° | **Parallelogram** | • opposite sides are equal in length<br>• opposite sides are parallel<br>• opposite angles are equal<br>• diagonals bisect each other |
| **Kite**  | • 2 pairs of sides are equal in length<br>• no parallel sides<br>• 1 pair of equal angles<br>• diagonals bisect each other at 90° | **Trapezium** | • 1 pair of parallel sides |
| | | **Isosceles trapezium**  | • 2 sides are equal in length<br>• 1 pair of parallel sides<br>• 2 pairs of equal angles |

**1** Name each quadrilateral being described.

**a** I have one pair of parallel sides.
Each of my sides is a different length. ..................................................

**b** All my angles are 90°.
My diagonals bisect at 90°. ..................................................

**2** One of the diagonals has been drawn in this rectangle.

Work out the sizes of angles $x$, $y$ and $z$. Give a reason for each answer

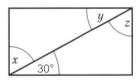

All angles in a rectangle are 90°.
Angles in a triangle sum to 180°.

**3 a** Quadrilateral PQRS is called an arrowhead.
Complete these statements

   **i** PS is equal in length to ........................

   **ii** PQ is equal in length to ........................

   **iii** ∠QPS = ∠........................

**b** In this arrowhead ∠RSQ = 40° and ∠QRS = 35°.
Calculate the size of these angles.

   **i** ∠QPS ........................

   **ii** ∠SQP ........................

   **iii** ∠PQR ........................

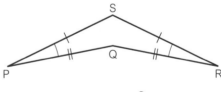

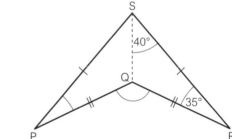

**Check** Tick each box as your **confidence** in this topic improves.

**Need extra help?** Go to page 87 and tick the boxes next to Q1–3. Then try them once you've finished 9.1–9.3.

84

**1 Reasoning**

  **a** Mark the two pairs of alternate angles.
Use a different colour for each pair.

  **b** Mark the four pairs of corresponding angles.
Use a different colour for each pair.

The blue angles are **alternate angles**. They are on different (alternate) sides of the diagonal line. The orange angles are **corresponding angles**. They are on the same (corresponding) sides of the diagonal line.

**2** Write the sizes of angles $a - c$.
Give a reason for each answer.

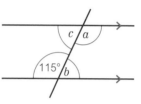

$a = $ ............... (alternate angle with ...............°)

$b = $ ............... $- 115° = $ ............... (angles on a straight line)

$c = $ ............... (alternate angle with $b$)

**3** Write the sizes of angles $a - i$.
Give a reason for each answer.

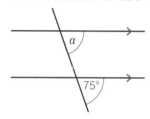
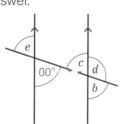
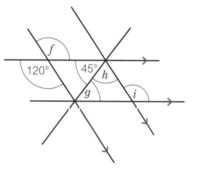

$a = $ ............... (corresponding angle with 75°)

$b = $ ............... (corresponding angles are .....................................)

$c = $ ............... (vertically opposite angles are ...............................)

$d = $ ........................................................................................

$e = $ ........................................................................................

$f = $ ........................................................................................

$g = $ ........................................................................................

$h = $ ........................................................................................

$i = $ ........................................................................................

When a line crosses two parallel lines it creates an 'F' shape.
Corresponding angles are equal.
Corresponding angles are on the same (corresponding) side of the diagonal line.

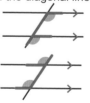

**Check**    Tick each box as your **confidence** in this topic improves.

**Need extra help?** Go to page 87 and tick the boxes next to Q4 and 5. Then try them once you've finished 9.1–9.3.

85

# Angles in polygons

A polygon is a closed shape with straight sides. In a regular polygon, the sides and angles are all equal.
Every polygon has exterior angles, $e$, and interior angles, $i$.

| Equilateral triangle | Square | Regular pentagon | Regular hexagon | Regular polygon of $n$ sides |
|---|---|---|---|---|
|  |  |  |  | |
| $3e = 360°$ | $4e = 360°$ | $5e = 360°$ | $6e = 360°$ | $ne = 360°$ |
| $3i = 180°$ | $4i = 360°$ | $5i = 540°$ | $6i = 720°$ | $ni = 180° \times (n - 2)$ |

**1 Problem-solving** The sum of the interior angles of a polygon is 1260°.
Work out how many sides it has.

 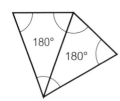 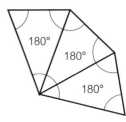

> 3 sides = 180°, 4 sides = 2 × 180 = 360°, 5 sides = 3 × 180 = 540°,
> ............... sides = ............... × 180 = 1260°

**2** Work out the interior angle of a regular pentagon.

Sum of interior angles
of an $n$-sided polygon
$S = (n - 2) \times 180°$

> $S = 180 \times (n - 2) = 180 \times (5 - 2) = 180 \times 3 = 540°$
> There are 5 equal interior angles, so each interior angle = ............. ÷ ............. = .............°

**3 Reasoning**

**a** What is the sum of the exterior angles of a regular decagon? ...............

A decagon
has 10 sides.

**b** Work out the size of one of its exterior angles.   360 ÷ ............... = ...............°

**c** Work out the size of one of its interior angles. ...............

**4 Problem-solving** The exterior angle of a regular polygon is 18°.

☐ × 18° = ☐°

**a** Work out the interior angle. ...............

**b** How many sides does the polygon have? ...............

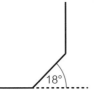

18°

**5** A regular polygon has 60 sides. Work out the size of its

**a** exterior angle

**b** interior angle.

**Worked
example**

**Check**   Tick each box as your **confidence** in this topic improves.
☹ 😐 🙂
☐ ☐ ☐

**Need extra help?** Go to page 88 and tick the boxes next to Q6–8. Then try them once you've finished 9.1–9.3.

86

## Quadrilaterals

**1** Match the quadrilateral with the description.

| **A** Parallelogram | **1** All sides and angles are equal |
| **B** Square | **2** One pair of parallel lines |
| **C** Trapezium | **3** Two pairs of parallel lines and diagonals bisect each other |

**2** Work out the angles marked with letters.

**Guided**

$d$ = .....° (opposite angles of a parallelogram)

$e$ = .....° (alternate angles)

$f$ = .....° (angle sum of a triangle)

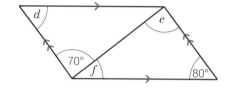

**3** Calculate the size of angle AFB.
Show your steps for solving this problem.
Explain your reasoning.

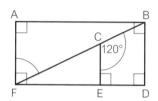

**Strategy hint**

Work out any angles you can and mark them on the diagram.

## Angles and parallel lines

**4** The diagram shows a set of parallel lines.

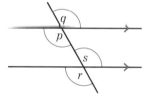

Complete these statements using words from the box.

**a** $p$ and $q$ are ................................................ angles

**b** $p$ and $s$ are ................................................ angles

**c** $p$ and $r$ are ................................................ angles

**d** $q$ and $s$ are ................................................ angles

**e** $r$ and $s$ are ................................................ angles

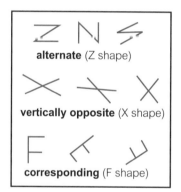

alternate (Z shape)

vertically opposite (X shape)

corresponding (F shape)

**5** Write the sizes of angles marked with letters in these diagrams.

Give a reason for each answer.

**Strategy hint**

In part **b**, look at the angles on each diagonal separately.

**a**

**Guided**

$p$ = ................... (alternate angles ...................)

**b**

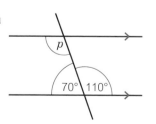

$q$ = ................... (corresponding angles ...................)

$r$ = ................... (vertically opposite angles ...................)

$s$ = ................... (corresponding angles ...................)

$t$ = ................... (angles on a straight line ...................)

## Angles in polygons

**Guided**

**6** Follow these steps to find the angle sum of a polygon.

1  Sketch the polygon.

2  Hold your pencil on one vertex.

3  Draw lines to the other vertices.

4  Write 180° in each triangle.

5  Work out the total, e.g. $4 \times 180° = $ .........°

Use this method to find the angle sums of each polygon in the table.

180°
180°
180°
180°

| Polygon | Angle sum |
|---------|-----------|
| square | |
| pentagon | |
| hexagon | $4 \times 180 = $ .........° |
| heptagon | |
| octagon | |

**7** Salem measured the exterior angles of this hexagon and added them together.

Explain how you know that her measurements are wrong.

What should the exterior angles add up to?

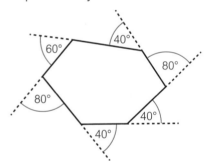

60°
40°
80°
80°
40°
40°

**8 Problem-solving** The exterior angle of a regular polygon is 20°.

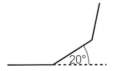

20°

The exterior angles add up to 360°.

☐ × 20° = 360°

**a** How many exterior angles does the polygon have? .......................

**b** How many sides does the polygon have? .......................

1 **Problem-solving** This pattern is made up of three identical yellow isosceles triangular tiles and three identical white isosceles triangular tiles.

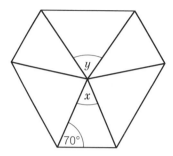

   **a** Work out the size of angle $x$. ........................

   **b** Work out the size of angle $y$. Show your working.

2 **Problem-solving** The diagram shows quadrilateral PQRS.

Work out the size of $\angle$QRT.

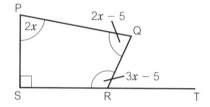

3 **Problem-solving** The diagram shows a shape made from five identical parallelograms.

Work out the size of angle $a$.

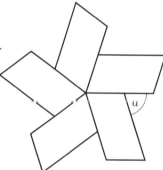

4 The diagram shows two overlapping regular hexagons.

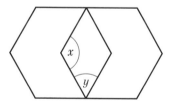

   **a** Work out the size of angle $x$. ................................................................

   **b** Work out the size of angle $y$. ................................................................

5 The diagram shows two lines intersecting a pair of parallel lines. Work out the sizes of angles $a - e$.

Give reasons for each.

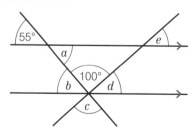

$a$ ...............................................................................................................

$b$ ...............................................................................................................

$c$ ...............................................................................................................

$d$ ...............................................................................................................

$e$ ...............................................................................................................

**6** Work out the sizes of the angles marked with letters.
Give reasons for your working.

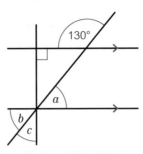

Use line symmetry
in your calculations.

**7 Reasoning** Here are three regular polygons.
Work out the sizes of the angles marked with letters.
Give a reason for each answer.

**a** 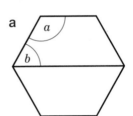     **b** 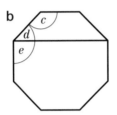     **c**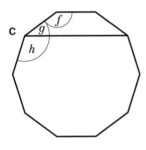

$a$ ........................

$b$ ........................

$c$ ........................

$d$ ........................

$e$ ........................

$f$ ........................

$g$ ........................

$h$ ........................

**8** A chiliagon is a polygon with 1000 sides. For a regular chiliagon, work out

    **a** the exterior angle        **b** the interior angle.

**9** Work out the angle, $x$, at the centre of each regular polygon.

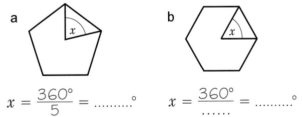

**a**        **b**        **c**

Angle at the centre of an
$n$-sided regular polygon $= \frac{360°}{n}$

$x = \dfrac{360°}{5} = ..........°$     $x = \dfrac{360°}{......} = ..........°$     ........................

**Guided**

**10 Reasoning** The diagram shows
a polygon in the shape of a star.
Angle $x$ is 30°. Work out the size of angle $y$.

Work out the
sum of the
interior angles.

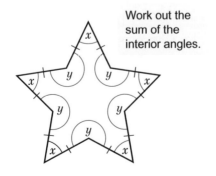

1 A quadrilateral has two pairs of equal sides, one pair of equal angles, one line of symmetry and rotational symmetry of order 1. What is its name? ..............................................................

2 Work out the size of angle $a$. Give a reason for your answer.

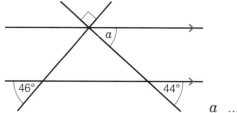

$a$ ........................

3 In this rectangle work out the size of ∠DBE.
Show your steps for solving the problem.
Give your reasons.

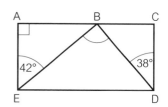

4 Work out the sizes of the angles marked with letters.
Give a reason for each answer.

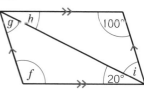

5 The diagram shows the exterior angles of a polygon.

   **a** Work out angle $j$. ........................
   **b** Work out the sum of the interior angles.

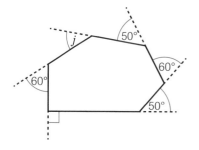

6 **a** Work out the exterior angle of a regular 36-sided polygon. ....................................................
   **b** Work out the interior angle of a regular 36-sided polygon. ....................................................

7 A regular polygon has an exterior angle of 30°.
   How many sides does the polygon have? ........................

**Guided**

1 The table shows the numbers of goals scored in the games in a hockey competition.
Work out the mean number of goals scored.

| Goals scored | Frequency | Total number of goals |
|:---:|:---:|:---:|
| 0 | 4 | $0 \times 4 = 0$ |
| 1 | 7 | $1 \times 7 = .....$ |
| 2 | 13 | $2 \times .... = .....$ |
| 3 | 6 | ........................ |
| Total | 30 | .......... |

Add a column to the table to work out the total number of goals.

Work out the total frequency (number of games at the competition) and the total number of goals.

**Worked example**

Mean = total number of goals ÷ number of games = ...........................................

2 **Problem-solving** The average number of children per family in the UK is 1.7.

The table shows the numbers of children per family in Year 8 in one school.

Are there more or fewer children per family in this Year 8 than on average in the UK? Explain your answer.

| Number of children in the family | Frequency |
|:---:|:---:|
| 1 | 67 |
| 2 | 77 |
| 3 | 24 |
| 4 | 7 |

3 This two-way table shows the numbers of vegetarian and non-vegetarian meals sold in a restaurant in one week.

| | Vegetarian | Non-vegetarian | Total |
|:---|:---:|:---:|:---:|
| Adult | 145 | 575 | 720 |
| Child | 36 | 144 | |
| Total | 181 | | |

A two-way table divides data into groups using rows across the table and columns down the table. You can calculate the totals across and down.

a Work out the total number of non-vegetarian meals sold. ....................

b How many child meals were sold? ....................

c How many meals were sold altogether? ....................

d What fraction of the meals sold were adult meals? ....................

4 **STEM** Wooden axe handles are made by a machine. Each handle should be 91 cm long.

Earl has accurately measured 20 axe handles and started a table for the results.

a The first class includes all lengths from 89 cm up to, but not including, 90 cm.
Which class contains the length 90.0 cm? ...........................................

b Complete the table, tallying these lengths in cm.
92.1, 91.6, 91.0, 89.9, 90.6, 90.8, 91.3

c Fill in the frequency column.   d Which is the modal class? ...........................................

| Length, $l$ (cm) | Tally | Frequency |
|:---:|:---:|:---:|
| $89 \leqslant l < 90$ | \| | |
| $90 \leqslant l < 91$ | \|\|\|\| | |
| $91 \leqslant l < 92$ | ⅢⅠ | |
| $92 \leqslant l < 93$ | \|\| | |

**Check** Tick each box as your **confidence** in this topic improves.

**Need extra help?** Go to page 97 and tick the boxes next to Q1–3. Then try them once you've finished 10.1–10.5.

**1** These sets of data are written in order.

   **a** 1, 1, 3, 4, 6, 6, 9

   **b** −9, −6, −6, 0, 0, 3, 4, 5,
      6, 8, 12, 13, 15, 15

In a set of 7 data values, the median is the $\frac{7+1}{2}$ = 4th value.

In a set of 8 data values, the median is the $\frac{8+1}{2} = \frac{9}{2}$ = 4.5th value.

In a set of $n$ data values, the median is the $\frac{n+1}{2}$th value.

For each set

   **i** count the number of values, $n$

   **ii** work out $\dfrac{n+1}{2}$ to find the middle value

   **iii** write down the median.

|  | Set a | Set b |
|---|---|---|
|  | ............. | ............. |
|  | ............. | ............. |
|  | ............. | ............. |

**2** Miguel grows limes. He finds the mass, in grams, of a random selection of his limes.

A stem and leaf diagram shows numerical data split into a 'stem' and 'leaves'. The key shows you how to read the values.

55, 56, 70, 52, 53, 63, 58, 49, 55, 60, 49,
51, 66, 72, 64, 58, 48, 53, 58, 72, 61

**a** Construct a stem and leaf diagram for this data.

**Guided**

```
4 |
5 | 5, 6, 2, 3
6 |
7 | 0
```

Decide on a stem. Write the leaves as you work along the data list and cross off each data item as you go. The next one to add is 63.

```
4 |
5 |
6 |
7 |
```

Write out your diagram again, putting the leaves in order.

Key: ...... | ...... means ...... grams —— Include a key for the stem and leaf diagrams.

**b Problem-solving** Use your diagram to answer these.

   **i** How many limes did Miguel weigh? ..............

   **ii** How many limes had a mass of more than 52 g? ..............

   Miguel sells limes as 'average' if they have a mass from 53 g to 63 g.

   **iii** What percentage of Miguel's limes are 'average'?

**3** The stem and leaf diagram shows the arm span of some Year 8 students, measured to the nearest centimetre.

```
13 | 8, 9, 9
14 | 0, 3, 4, 5, 5, 5, 6, 8
15 | 0, 1, 2, 2, 4, 4, 6, 7, 7, 8
16 | 1, 2, 2, 4, 9
```

Key: 13 | 8 means 138 cm

Write down

**a** the mode ..............

**b** the range ...................................

**c** the median. ..............

To find the mode, look for the repeated values. The range is biggest value − smallest value. The median is the $\frac{n+1}{2}$th value.

**Check** Tick each box as your **confidence** in this topic improves.

**Need extra help?** Go to page 98 and tick the box next to Q4. Then try it once you've finished 10.1–10.5.

93

**Guided**

**1** Some students were asked whether global climate change was actually happening.
The table shows the students' replies.
Draw a pie chart to show this data.

Number of students = 18 + 4 + 14 = 36

| Reply | Frequency | Angle |
|-------|-----------|-------|
| Yes | 18 | |
| No | 4 | |
| Unsure | 14 | |

÷ 36 $\left(\begin{array}{c}\text{36 students are } 360°\\ \text{1 student is } 10°\end{array}\right)$ ÷ 36

1 Work out the total frequency.
2 Work out the angle for one student.
3 Work out the angle for each set of replies.
4 Check that the angles add up to 360°.

Angle for 'Yes':

× 18 $\left(\begin{array}{c}\text{1 student is } 10°\\ \text{18 students are } 180°\end{array}\right)$ × 18

Angle for 'No' = 4 × .............. = ..............°

Angle for 'Unsure' = ..............°

Check: 180° + ..............° + ..............° = 360° ✓

A pie chart is a circle divided into slices called
sectors. The whole circle represents a set of data.
Each sector represents a fraction of the data.

Students' replies

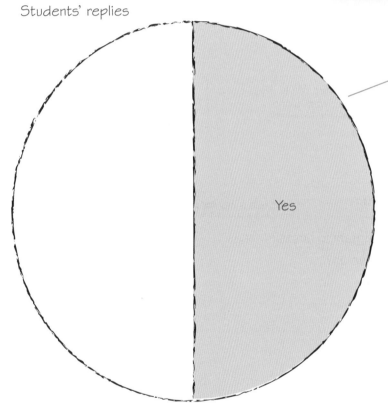

Yes

Draw the pie chart.
Draw in a radius.
Then use a protractor to draw the
angles.
Label each sector or make a key
(you do not have to label the angles).
Give your pie chart a title.

**Worked
example**

**2** Pablo needs to draw a pie chart for each of these tables of results.
Work out the angles for him.

**a**

| Pet | Frequency | Angle |
|-----|-----------|-------|
| Cat | 6 | |
| Parrot | 10 | |
| Other | 2 | |

**b**

| Car | Percentage | Angle |
|-----|------------|-------|
| BMW | 25% | |
| Ford | 25% | |
| Seat | 40% | |
| Lotus | 10% | |

**Check** Tick each box as your
**confidence** in this
topic improves.

☹ 😐 ☺

**Need extra help?** Go to page 98 and tick
the box next to Q5. Then try it once you've
finished 10.1–10.5.

**Guided**

1 **Real / Reasoning** The graph shows the scores of the winning and losing teams for the last 12 basketball games watched by Leslie.

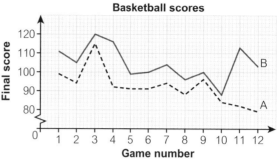

**Basketball scores**

a One line shows the winning team's scores. Which one?   The ...........est of the two lines.

b In which week(s) was the difference between the winning and losing scores

   i the greatest   In game number 11, points are the furthest apart; difference is 113 − ............ = ............

   ii the smallest?   ...............................................................................................................................

c Leslie says, 'The winning teams' scores are all higher than any of the losing teams' scores.' Is he correct? Explain.

2 The table shows the number of cushions made each Monday during July at two factories.

| | Monday 7th | Monday 14th | Monday 21st | Monday 28th |
|---|---|---|---|---|
| Factory A | 7700 | 7550 | 3750 | 8000 |
| Factory B | 7200 | 7200 | 7300 | 7700 |

a From the results table, which factory do you think can make the most cushions in one day? ...........

b Calculate the mean number of cushions made by

   i factory A ........................   ii factory B. ........................

c Calculate the median number of cushions made by

   i factory A ........................   ii factory B. ........................

d Which average, the mean or median, better represents the performance of

   i factory A ........................   ii factory B. ........................

e i **Reasoning** Which value affected factory A's mean number of cushions? ....................

   ii Why didn't it affect the median?

**Literacy hint**

A data value that doesn't 'fit' with the other values is called an outlier.

3 Here are the times, in seconds, taken by eight students to solve a puzzle.

127, 139, 99, 130, 18, 146, 104, 133

**Worked example**

a One student had seen the puzzle before. Which time was probably theirs? ...........

b Work out the mean time. ...................................................................................

c Work out the median time. ...............................................................................

d Which represents the average time better, the mean or the median? ..................

e Which average would the teacher use to show that they teach puzzle-solving well?

**Check**   Tick each box as your **confidence** in this topic improves.   ☹ 😐 ☺   **Need extra help?** Go to page 98 and tick the box next to Q6. Then try it once you've finished 10.1–10.5.

95

**1 STEM / Reasoning** The table shows the concentration level of medication in the blood of 12 volunteers, in milligrams per litre, and their reaction time to do a simple task.

| Concentration (mg/l) | 6 | 50 | 70 | 42 | 2 | 60 | 50 | 28 | 40 | 30 | 14 | 76 |
|---|---|---|---|---|---|---|---|---|---|---|---|---|
| Time (s) | 1.4 | 2.0 | 5.2 | 4.1 | 1.7 | 4.0 | 4.5 | 3.0 | 3.5 | 3.5 | 2.0 | 5.1 |

**a** Draw a scatter graph to show this data.
 Give the chart a title.

A **scatter graph** shows two sets of data on the same graph. The shape of a scatter graph shows if there is a relationship or **correlation** between two sets of data.

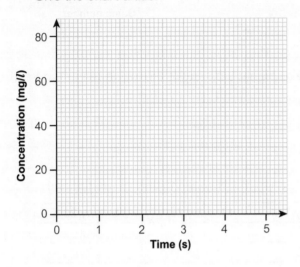

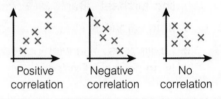

Positive correlation  Negative correlation  No correlation

**b** Describe the correlation shown by the scatter graph. ...............................................................

**c** Write down the concentration level of medication of the person who took 4 seconds. ..................

**d** Kabali thinks one point has been plotted incorrectly. Which point do you think this is? Explain.

A line of best fit shows the relationship between two sets of data.
There should be about the same number of crosses on each side of the line.
There may also be crosses on the line. A good line here would be from (1.6, 0) to (5.4, 76).

**e** Draw a line of best fit.

**f** Use your line of best fit to estimate the concentration level of medicine of someone who takes 4 seconds. ...............

Draw a line upwards from 4 seconds to the line of best fit. Then draw a line across and read off the concentrations.

**2 STEM / Real** The table shows the width and length of 7 razor clam shells.

| Width (cm) | 1.3 | 2.1 | 2.3 | 2.8 | 3.0 | 3.4 | 3.6 |
|---|---|---|---|---|---|---|---|
| Length (cm) | 6.0 | 9.6 | 10.2 | 12.8 | 13.4 | 15.0 | 16.2 |

**a** Draw a scatter graph for this data.

**b** Draw a line of best fit on your scatter graph.

**c** Use your line of best fit to estimate

 **i** the length of a 2.5 cm wide shell ...............

 **ii** the width of a 12 cm long shell. ...............

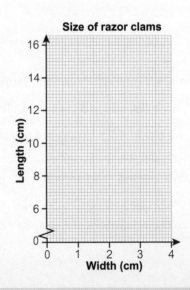

**Check** Tick each box as your **confidence** in this topic improves.

**Need extra help?** Go to page 98 and tick the box next to Q7. Then try it once you've finished 10.1–10.5.

96

## Using tables

**1** Faadl and Maahir are comparing the photos and videos on their phones. Faadl had 24 photos and 11 videos, whilst Maahir had 29 photos and 5 videos.

A two-way table splits data into groups in rows across the table and in columns down the table. You can calculate the totals across and down.

    **a** Write Faadl's data in the top row of the two-way table. Work out the total.

    **b** Write Maahir 's data in the second row.

    **c** Work out the total of each column.

|  | Photos | Videos | Total |
|---|---|---|---|
| Faadl | 24 | 11 | |
| Maahir | | | |
| Total | | | |

    **d** Add the row totals together. Check by adding the column totals together.

**2** Ellie asked the students in her class how many siblings (brothers and sisters) they each have. The frequency table shows her results.

    **a** How many students have 4 siblings? ...............

    **b** How many students have 3 or more siblings?

    .........................................................................

    **c** How many students did Ellie ask altogether?

    .........................................................................

| Number of siblings | Frequency | Siblings × Frequency |
|---|---|---|
| 0 | 8 | $0 \times 8 = 0$ |
| 1 | 13 | $1 \times 13 = 13$ |
| 2 | 5 | $2 \times \ldots = \ldots$ |
| 3 | 3 | $\ldots \times \ldots = \ldots$ |
| 4 | 1 | $\ldots \times \ldots = \ldots$ |
| Total | ..... | ..... |

    **d** Work out the range of the number of siblings.

    .........................................................................

    **e** Complete the table.

    **f** Calculate the mean number of siblings.

$$\text{Mean} = \frac{\text{total number of siblings}}{\text{total number of students}}$$

**Guided**

**3** Here are the heights, $h$, of the members of a hockey team.

    153 cm, 136 cm, 150 cm, 135 cm, 141 cm, 139 cm, 144 cm, 149 cm, 151 cm, 143 cm, 154 cm

    **a** What does $135 \leqslant h < 140$ mean? ...................................................................

    **b** Complete the table. Tally the heights into it. Complete the frequency column.

    **c** Which is the modal class? ................................

        Write the class like this: ☐ cm $\leqslant h <$ ☐ cm

| Height, $h$ (cm) | Tally | Frequency |
|---|---|---|
| $135 \leqslant h < 140$ | | |
| $140 \leqslant h < 145$ | | |
| $145 \leqslant h < 150$ | | |
| $150 \leqslant h < 155$ | | |

## Presenting and comparing data

**4** The stem and leaf diagram shows the ages of people using a gym one morning.

    **a** What does 6 | 5 mean? .........................

    **b** How many people in their 60s were in the gym? ...............

    **c** How many people were in the gym? ...............

    **d** What was the mode? ...............

    **e** Imagine all the people lined up in order of age, holding numbers 1, 2, 3, 4, 5, ... What number would the middle person be holding? .........

    **f** Use your answer to part **e** to help you find the median age from the stem and leaf diagram.

| | |
|---|---|
| 3 | 2, 8 |
| 4 | 0, 2, 7, 8, 9 |
| 5 | 1, 2, 2, 2, 6, 8 |
| 6 | 0, 0, 2, 5, 6, 6, 7, 8, 8 |
| 7 | 2, 2, 7 |

Key:  3 | 2 means 32

How many values are in the 6 | ... row?

The 1st person is 32, the 2nd person is 38 and so on.

**5** The table shows the favourite yoghurt flavours of 15 students.

| Flavour | Frequency | Sector angle |
|---|---|---|
| Vanilla | 5 | |
| Strawberry | 2 | |
| Lemon | 1 | |
| Toffee | 7 | |

**Yoghurt flavour preference**

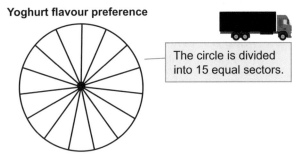

The circle is divided into 15 equal sectors.

**a** Work out the angle of one sector.

$360° ÷ 15 = $ ............

**b** How many sectors would you shade for lemon flavour? ............

**c** How many sectors would you shade for strawberry flavour? ............

**d** Complete the column of sector angles. Check that they add up to 360°.

**e** Complete the pie chart to show the favourite yoghurt flavours.

**6 Reasoning** The table shows the median weight and the range of the weights of the boys and girls in two schools.

| | Median | Range |
|---|---|---|
| **Boys** | 51 kg | 15 kg |
| **Girls** | 49 kg | 11 kg |

**a** Choose the words in the box to complete these sentences comparing the weights of the two genders.

The boys had a ........................ median than the girls.

The girls had a ........................ range than the boys,

so their weights were ........................ consistent.

larger
less
more
smaller

**b** Write two sentences comparing the findings.

## Scatter graphs

**7** In an experiment, students were allowed different amounts of time to study for a test.

| Mistakes | 52 | 47 | 38 | 41 | 35 | 29 | 11 | 19 | 10 | 6 |
|---|---|---|---|---|---|---|---|---|---|---|
| Time (hours) | 1 | 1 | 1.5 | 2 | 2 | 2.5 | 3 | 3 | 3.5 | 4 |

The table shows the number of mistakes they each made.

**a** Draw a scatter graph for the data on the grid.

**b** There is a ........................ correlation between the number of mistakes made and studying time.

**c** Draw a straight line of best fit.

**d** Use your line of best fit to estimate the number of mistakes made after 2 hours of study. ........................

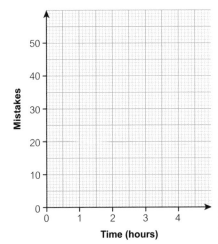

**Worked example**

Positive correlation: looking from the vertical axis, the points go 'uphill': the values are increasing.
Negative correlation: looking from the vertical axis, the points go 'downhill': the values are decreasing.
No correlation: the points are not close to a straight line, uphill or downhill.

**1** The table shows the masses, $m$ kg, of a class of Year 7 students in a boys' school and a class of Year 7 students in a girls' school.

  **a** Complete the grouped frequency table.

|  | 25 ≤ $m$ < 35 | 35 ≤ $m$ < 45 | 45 ≤ $m$ < 55 | Total |
|---|---|---|---|---|
| **Boys** | 7 | 6 | 3 |  |
| **Girls** | 3 | 7 | 4 |  |
| **Total** |  |  |  |  |

  **b** How many boys have a mass of at least 35 kg? .......................

  **c** Compare the average masses of the boys and the girls.

**2** **Problem-solving** The pie charts show the views of a group of 160 students from a boys' school and 200 students from a girls' school on the amount of homework given.

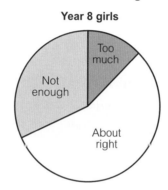

**Year 8 boys** — Too much, Not enough, About right

**Year 8 girls** — Too much, Not enough, About right

  **a** How many boys said they had too much homework? .......................

  **b** Aleem says, 'More girls than boys said they had too much homework.'

   Is he correct? Show your working.

**3** **Reasoning** Sophie and Aidan are spinning a 5-sided spinner as part of a game – the higher the score, the better. The tables show the outcomes of the game.

| Sophie | |
|---|---|
| **Score** | **Frequency** |
| 1 | 4 |
| 2 | 3 |
| 3 | 6 |
| 4 | 7 |
| 5 | 5 |

| Aidan | |
|---|---|
| **Score** | **Frequency** |
| 1 | 6 |
| 2 | 4 |
| 3 | 6 |
| 4 | 4 |
| 5 | 5 |

  **a** Calculate the mean for each player.

  **b** Which player did better? Justify your answer.

**4** Here are the numbers of words in the poems that tutor group 8B studied for homework.

320, 256, 458, 578, 582, 414, 476, 376, 225, 121, 137, 294,
409, 518, 327, 319, 626, 488, 534, 496, 282, 584, 367, 196

**Worked example**

**a** Draw a sorted stem and leaf diagram for the data.
Use the key '1 | 21 means 121 words'.

**b** How many students are in tutor group 8B? ........................

**c** What percentage of the poems had over 500 words? ........................

**d** Draw a grouped frequency table for this data.
Use the classes $100 < w \leqslant 200$, $200 < w \leqslant 300$, etc.

**e** Use the data, the stem and leaf diagram and your frequency table to find

  **i** the median number of words ........................   **ii** the mean number of words ........................

  **iii** the range ........................               **iv** the modal class. ........................

**5 STEM / Modelling**

The temperature at which pure water boils changes with altitude (height). This scatter graph shows the results of experiments boiling water at different altitudes.

**a** Describe the correlation shown by the graph. ..............................................

**b** What happens to the boiling point of water as the altitude increases?

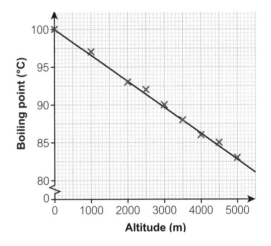

**c** What is the boiling point of water at 5000 m? ..............................................

**d** Use the line of best fit to predict the boiling point of water at 1600 m. ........................................

**e** Denver, USA, is at an altitude of 1600 m and La Rinconada, Peru, is at an altitude of 5000 m.
Using your answers from parts **c** and **d**, estimate the difference in the boiling point of water between Denver and La Rinconada.

**1** The pie chart shows the different surfboards sold at a surf shop one summer. In total 108 surfboards were sold.

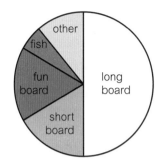

How many of the surfboards sold were

**a** long boards ..........................................

**b** fun boards ..........................................

**c** fish? ..........................................

**2** A survey asked people how many mobile phones they owned. The results are in the table.

**a** Work out the range. ..........................................

**b** What is the mode? ..........................................

**c** Work out the mean. Give your answer to one decimal place.

| Phones owned | Frequency |
|:---:|:---:|
| 0 | 2 |
| 1 | 23 |
| 2 | 17 |
| 3 | 3 |

**3** Pilots do a test during their training to measure their reaction times.

The stem and leaf diagram shows the reaction times of some pilots.

**a** What is the range? ..........................

**b** What is the median? ..........................

| 5 | 2, 3 |
|:---:|:---|
| 6 | 0, 1, 8, 9 |
| 7 | 4, 4, 5, 6, 8 |
| 8 | 1 |
| 9 | 2, 2, 5 |

Key: 5 | 2 means 5.2 seconds

**4** The table shows the numbers of students late to school during 2 weeks.

|  | Mon | Tue | Wed | Thu | Fri |
|:---|:---:|:---:|:---:|:---:|:---:|
| Week 1 | 7 | 8 | 9 | 9 | 32 |
| Week 2 | 13 | 13 | 12 | 15 | 15 |

**a** On one day the school bus broke down. Which day do you think this was? Explain your answer.

**b** For each week, work out

**i** the median ........................ **ii** the mean ........................ **iii** the range. ........................

**5** The table shows the pulse and breathing rates (per minute) of ten people during different activities.

| Pulses per minute | 62 | 68 | 72 | 75 | 85 | 84 | 90 | 88 | 96 |
|:---|:---:|:---:|:---:|:---:|:---:|:---:|:---:|:---:|:---:|
| Breaths per minute | 17 | 19 | 21 | 21 | 25 | 27 | 29 | 29 | 31 |

**a** Draw a scatter graph for the data using these axes.

**b** Describe the correlation between breathing rate and pulse rate. ..........................................

**c** Draw a line of best fit.

**d** Val has a pulse rate of 80 per minute.

Estimate her breathing rate. ....................................

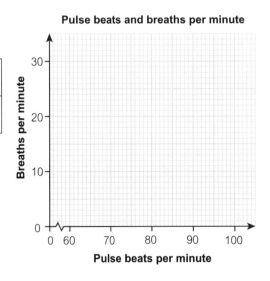

**Pulse beats and breaths per minute**

Breaths per minute (y-axis): 0, 10, 20, 30

Pulse beats per minute (x-axis): 0, 60, 70, 80, 90, 100

**1** The equation of a line is $9y - 12x = 18$.

**a** Work out $y$ when $x = 0$.

When $x = 0$:

$9y - 12 \times 0 = 18$

$9y = 18$

$y = \dots$

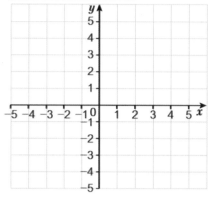

Substitute $x = 0$ into the equation. Solve to find the value of $y$.

**b** Work out $x$ when $y = 0$.

When $y = 0$:

Substitute $y = 0$ into the equation. Solve to find the value of $x$.

**c** Plot and label the graph on the grid.

| $x$ | | |
|-----|--|--|
| $y$ | | |

Draw a table of values with $x = 0$ and $y = 0$.

The $y$-intercept is where a line crosses the $y$-axis.
To find the $y$-intercept of a graph, find the $y$-coordinate where $x = 0$.
To find the $x$-intercept of a graph, find the $x$-coordinate where $y = 0$.

**2** On this grid plot and label the graphs of

**a** $x + y = 3$

**b** $x - y = 2$

**c** $2x - 10y = 5$

**d** $5y = 2x - 3$

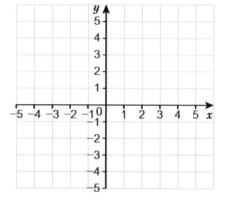

Use the method you used in Q1.

**Worked example**

**3** Work out the $y$-intercept for each line.

**a** $y = 2x - 5$ ..............

**b** $y = -\dfrac{1}{2}x + 2$ ..............

**c** $y = x$ ..............

**4** **Reasoning** Match the equations to their graphs.

| Equation | Graph |
|----------|-------|
| $y = 4x + 1$ | |
| $y = -x + 2$ | |
| $y = x + \dfrac{1}{2}$ | |
| $y = \dfrac{1}{2}x - 2$ | |
| $y = -x - 3$ | |
| $y = 3x + 3$ | |

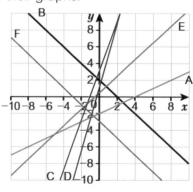

**5** Write the equations of three lines that go through the point (0, 2).

The equations all need to start $y =$

**Check**

Tick each box as your **confidence** in this topic improves.

**Need extra help?** Go to page 105 and tick the boxes next to Q1 and 2. Then try them once you've finished 11.1–11.3.

102

**Guided**

**1** Work out the gradient of each line.

**A** Gradient = 3

**B** ...............

**C** ...............

**D** ...............

The steepness of the graph is called the gradient.

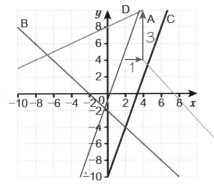

To find the gradient, work out how many units the graph goes up for every 1 unit across.

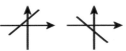

Gradients are positive (/, uphill) or negative (\, downhill).
The larger the value, the steeper the slope.

Choose a point on the line.
Draw a horizontal line 1 unit in the $x$-direction.
Draw a vertical line to the graph line.
When the $x$-value increases by 1, the $y$-value increases by the gradient.

**2** Draw lines on the grid with these gradients.

**a** 3  **b** −2  **c** $-\dfrac{1}{2}$  **d** $\dfrac{2}{3}$

**3** **Real / Modelling** An online photo printing company uses this equation to work out the cost of printing photographs:

$y = 2.5 + 0.05x$

where $x$ is the number of photographs being printed and $y$ is the total cost of the bill in pounds.

**a** Where does the line intersect the $y$-axis? ...............

**b** How much is the bill when there are no photographs being printed? ...............

**c** What is the gradient of the line? ...............

**d** How much does each photograph cost? ...............

**4** Plot and label these graphs.
Fill in the gradient and $y$-intercept in the table.

| Equation of line | Gradient | $y$-intercept |
|---|---|---|
| **a** $y = x + 2$ | | |
| **b** $y = -2x - 1$ | | |
| **c** $y = 3x - 2$ | | |
| **d** $y = -x + 3$ | | |
| **e** $y = \dfrac{1}{2}x$ | | |

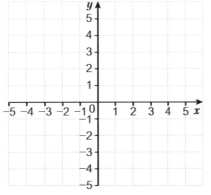

A linear equation generates a straight-line (linear) graph.

**Check** Tick each box as your **confidence** in this topic improves. ☹ 😐 ☺

**Need extra help?** Go to page 105 and tick the boxes next to Q3 and 4. Then try them once you've finished 11.1–11.3.

**1** Write the gradient and $y$-intercept of each line.

**a** $y = 3x - 2$

    gradient $= m = 3$

    $y$-intercept $= c = $ ..............

**b** $y = 2x$

**c** $y = -\frac{1}{2}x + 1$

> The equation of a straight-line graph can always be written in the form $y = mx + c$. $m$ is the gradient and $c$ is the $y$-intercept.

**2** Match the equations to the graphs.

| Equation | Graph |
|---|---|
| $y = 3x + 1$ | |
| $y = x + 2$ | |
| $y = \frac{1}{2}x$ | |
| $y = -2x - 3$ | |
| $y = \frac{1}{2}x - 2$ | |
| $y = 3x - 2$ | |

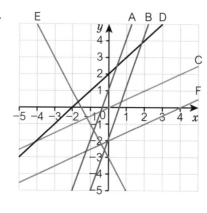

Worked example

**3** Write the equations of these graphs in order of increasing steepness.

**A** $y = x + 10$      **B** $y = 2x - 3$      **C** $y = 0.4x + 15$

**4** A line has equation $y = 2x + 3$.

**a** What is its $y$-intercept? .............. Plot it on the axis.

**b** What is its gradient? ..............

**c** Start at the $y$-intercept. Draw a straight line with this gradient. Extend your line to both edges of the grid. Label your line.

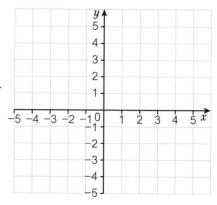

**5** Use the method and grid in Q4 to plot and label these graphs.

**a** $y = 3x - 4$      **b** $y = x + 2$

**c** $y = -2x + 1$      **d** $y = \frac{1}{2}x$

**6** $y = 3x - 1$

**a** Work out the value of $y$ when $x = 5$.
Complete the coordinates: $(5, $ .............. $)$.

**b** Does the point $(1, 1)$ lie on the line $y = 3x - 1$? ..............

> Substitute $x = 1$ into the equation of the line.

**7** **Problem-solving** Which of these points lie on each line?

A $(2, -3)$    B $(4, 14)$    C $(2, 7)$    D $(-1, 7)$    E $(-1, 1)$    F $(2, 8)$

**a** $y = 2x + 3$ ..............      **b** $y = x - 5$ ..............      **c** $2y = 6x + 4$ ..............

**Check**    Tick each box as your **confidence** in this topic improves.

**Need extra help?** Go to page 106 and tick the boxes next to Q5–9. Then try them once you've finished 11.1–11.3.

## Straight-line graphs

**1 a** Complete the table of values for $y = 3x + 2$.

| $x$ | −2 | −1 | 0 | 1 | 2 |
|-----|----|----|---|---|---|
| $3x$ | −6 | −3 | | | |
| $3x + 2$ | −4 | | | | |
| $y$ | −4 | | | | |

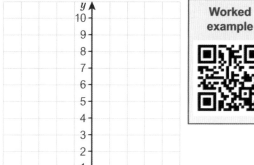

Worked example

**b** Write down the coordinate pairs.

(−2, −4), (−1, ....), ......................................

**c** Plot all the coordinates on the grid.
Join them with a straight line and label the line $y = 3x + 2$.

**2 a** Complete the table of values for $y = \frac{1}{2}x - 1$.

| $x$ | −2 | −1 | 0 | 1 | 2 |
|-----|----|----|---|---|---|
| $\frac{1}{2}x$ | | | | | |
| $\frac{1}{2}x - 1$ | | | | | |
| $y$ | | | | | |

**b** Use the grid in Q1 to draw and label the graph of $y = \frac{1}{2}x - 1$.

## Gradients

**3** The diagram shows four lines.

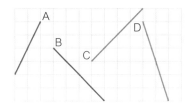

positive

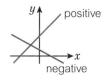
negative

**a** Which lines have a positive gradient? ............................

**b** Choose a point on line A.
Move your finger one square across (to the right).

  **i** How many squares does your finger move up to meet line A again? ....................

  **ii** What is the gradient of line A? ....................

**c** Repeat part **b** to work out the gradient of line

  **i** B ...............      **ii** C ...............      **iii** D ...............

**4** These lines have gradients which are fractions.
Write the gradient of each line.

How many equal steps does it take to go up one whole square?

**a**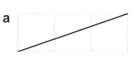

**b**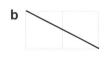

..............................      ..............................

## Finding the equation of a line

**5** Write the coordinates where each line intersects the $y$-axis.

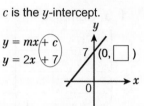

**a** $y = 2x + 7$ ...........................

**b** $y = x - 3$ ...........................

**c** $y = -2x - 5$ ...........................

**6** **a** Work out the gradient of line A. ...........................

**b** Write down the $y$-intercept of line A. ...................

The $y$-intercept is the value where the line crosses the $y$-axis.

**c** Complete the equation of line A.

$y = $ ......$x + $ ......

↑ ↑

gradient   $y$-intercept

**d** Complete the equation of line B.

$y = $ ......$x + $ ......

**e** Write down the equations of these lines.

**i** C ........................................

**ii** D ........................................

Decide if the gradient is positive or negative.

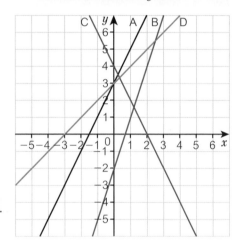

**7** Complete this table.

| Equation | Gradient | $y$-intercept |
|---|---|---|
| **a** $y = 2x + 5$ | 2 | (0, .....) |
| **b** $y = 5x - 4$ | | (..... , $-4$) |
| **c** $y = -4x - 1$ | $-4$ | (0, .....) |
| **d** $y = 3x$ | | (0, 0) |
| **e** $y = -3x + 7$ | | |
| **f** $y = x - 2$ | | |
| **g** $y = -4x + 5$ | | |

Gradient: $y = \textcircled{m}x + c$
$y$-intercept: $y = mx + \textcircled{c}$

**8** **a** Work out the gradient of this line. ......................................

**b** When $x = 0$, what is the value of $y$? ...................................

**c** Write the equation of the line in the form $y = mx + c$.

........................................

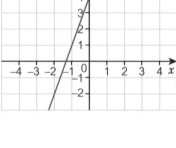

**9** Work out the equation of this line.

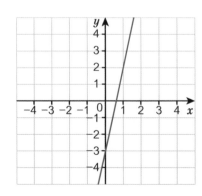

**Worked example**

**1 Reasoning**

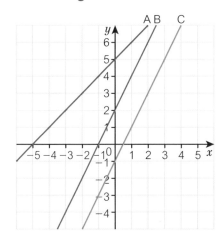

a Work out the gradient of line A. ............................

b Write down the $y$-intercept for line A. ............................

> The $y$-intercept is where a line crosses the $y$ axis.

c Use your answers to **a** and **b** to write the equation of line A.

$$y = \text{......} x + \text{......}$$

gradient   $y$-intercept

A linear equation generates a straight-line graph.
The equation for a straight-line graph can be written as $y = mx + c$ where $m$ is the gradient and $c$ is the $y$-intercept.

**Guided**

d Write the equation of line

  i B ............................        ii C ............................

e Lines B and C are parallel. What do you notice about their gradients? ............................

f On the grid with lines A, B and C, draw and label the graph of the equations

  i $y = 2x - 3$        ii $y = 2x$

**2 a** Work out the gradient of this line.

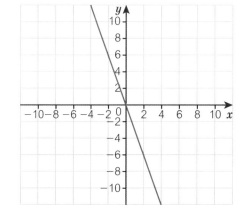

b Write the equation of the line in the form $y = mx + c$.

**3** A line has gradient 5. It goes through the point $(-2, 2)$.

a Write the equation of the line in the form $y = mx + c$, substituting the value for $m$.

b Substitute the values of $x$ and $y$ for the point $(-2, 2)$.

c Solve the equation you got in part **b** to find the value of $c$.

d Write the equation of the line. ............................

**4** A line has gradient −3. It goes through the point (3, 1).
What is the equation of the line?

**5** Find the gradient of the line joining each pair of points.

**a** (5, 5) and (7, 15)　　　　**b** (−4, 3) and (7, 9)

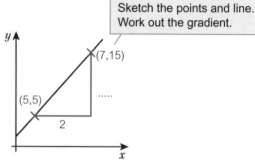

> Sketch the points and line.
> Work out the gradient.

**6** A straight line goes through the points (0, 1) and (2, 7).
Write the equation of the line.

> Work out the gradient.
> Use the $y$-intercept.

**7** An arithmetic sequence starts:　3, 7, 11, 15, ...

**a** Extend the graph to include as many terms as
you can.

**b** Write the equation of the line.

.................................................................

**c** Work out the $n$th term of the sequence
3, 7, 11, 15, ...
What do you notice?

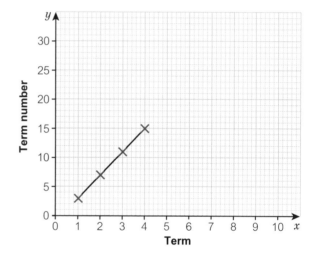

**d** What will the 20th term of the sequence be?

> Substitute $n = 20$ into
> the equation of the line.

**8 Problem-solving** The rectangle is made using
four straight lines.

**a** Which of the lines have the same
gradient? ...........................

**b** Write the equations of the four straight lines.

.................................................................................

.................................................................................

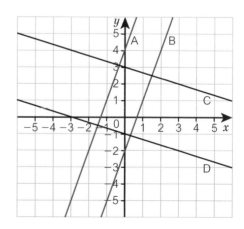

1 The equation of a line is $2y + 3x = 6$.

a Complete this table.

| $x$ | 0 | |
|---|---|---|
| $y$ | | |
| Coordinate | $(0, \ldots)$ | $(\ldots, 0)$ |

b Use the results from part **a** to draw the line $2y + 3x = 6$ on the grid.

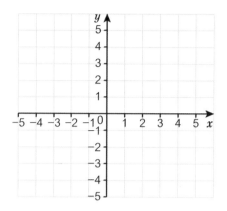

2 Here are the equations of four lines.

$y = 5x + 1 \qquad y = 3x + 7 \qquad y = 2x - 4 \qquad y = 3x - 4$

a Write down the equation of the steepest line. ...........................

b Which equations have the same gradients? ...................................................................

3 a Where does the line $y = 2x + 5$ cross the $y$-axis? ...........................

b What is the gradient of the line $y = -3x + 1$? ...........................

4 A line has gradient 5 and intersects the $y$-axis at $(0, -2)$.
Write the equation of the line. ...................................................................

5 Work out the gradient of each line.

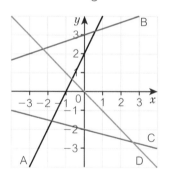

A ........................ B ........................ C ........................ D ........................

6 Work out the equation of each line in Q5.

A ........................ B ........................ C ........................ D ........................

7 Does the point $(3, 1)$ lie on the line $y = 3x - 10$?
Show working to explain.

# Progression charts

Progression is all about checking your confidence in the maths that you're learning.

- For each Unit test, tick the questions you answered correctly.
- Then rate your confidence by ticking a smiley face.

**1**  Number

| I can... | Unit 1: Unit test |
|---|---|
| Add, subtract, multiply and divide positive and negative numbers. | Q1 ☐  Q6 ☐ |
| Write the prime factor decomposition of a number and use it to find the HCF or LCM of two numbers. | Q2 ☐  Q4 ☐ |
| Use the laws of indices for multiplying and dividing. | Q3 ☐  Q7 ☐ |
| Carry out calculations involving powers, roots and brackets following the priority of operations. | Q5 ☐  Q6 ☐ |
| **My confidence**  ☹○  😐○  ☺○ | |

**2**  Equations and formulae

| I can... | Unit 2: Unit test |
|---|---|
| Write and solve one-step and two-step equations. | Q1 ☐  Q2 ☐  Q3 ☐ |
| Write and solve equations with letters on both sides. | Q5 ☐  Q6 ☐ |
| Find numbers which satisfy an equation with two unknowns. | Q7 ☐ |
| Solve problems by writing and using formulae. | Q4 ☐  Q8 ☐ |
| **My confidence**  ☹○  😐○  ☺○ | |

**3**  Working with powers

| I can... | Unit 3: Unit test |
|---|---|
| Understand the meaning of an identity. | Q6 ☐ |
| Use the index laws in algebraic calculations and expressions. | Q2 ☐  Q10 ☐ |
| Factorise an algebraic expression. | Q5 ☐  Q7 ☐ |
| Write and simplify expressions involving brackets and powers. | Q1 ☐  Q3 ☐  Q4 ☐ |
| Substitute integers into expressions. | Q8 ☐ |
| Solve equations involving brackets. | Q9 ☐ |
| **My confidence**  ☹○  😐○  ☺○ | |

**4** 2D shapes and 3D solids

| I can... | Unit 4: Unit test |
|---|---|
| Derive and use the formula for the area of a triangle and a parallelogram. | Q3 ☐ |
| Calculate the area of compound shapes made from rectangles and triangles. | Q1 ☐ |
| Calculate the volume and surface area of cubes and cuboids. | Q2 ☐ |
| Use 2D representations of 3D solids. | Q4 ☐ |
| Convert between metric measures for area and volume. | Q5 ☐ |
| Solve problems involving area, surface area and volume. | Q6 ☐ |
| **My confidence** ☹○ ☺○ ☺○ | |

**5** Graphs

| I can... | Unit 5: Unit test |
|---|---|
| Plot graphs and read values to solve problems. | Q3 ☐ |
| Recognise when values are in direct proportion | Q4 ☐ |
| Understand financial graphs. | Q5 ☐ |
| Use distance–time graphs to solve problems. | Q1 ☐ |
| Interpret real-life graphs. | Q2 ☐ |
| **My confidence** ☹○ ☺○ ☺○ | |

**6** Fractions, decimals, ratio and proportion

| I can... | Unit 6: Unit test |
|---|---|
| Round to decimal places. | Q1 ☐ |
| Multiply decimals using a written method. | Q2 ☐ |
| Convert fractions to decimals by dividing the numerator by the denominator. | Q5 ☐ |
| Convert recurring decimals to fractions using an algebraic method. | Q7 ☐ |
| Multiply and divide fractions. | Q3 ☐ Q4 ☐ |
| Use the four operations with mixed numbers. | Q6 ☐ |
| **My confidence** ☹○ ☺○ ☺○ | |

**7**  Probability

| I can... | Unit 7: Unit test | | | |
|---|---|---|---|---|
| Estimate probability based on experimental data. | Q1 ☐ | | | |
| Make conclusions based on the results of an experiment. | Q3 ☐ | | Q5 ☐ | |
| Use estimated probability to calculate expected frequencies. | Q2 ☐ | | Q4 ☐ | |
| **My confidence** ☹◯ ☺◯ ☺◯ | | | | |

**8**  Percentages and ratios

| I can... | Unit 8: Unit test | | |
|---|---|---|---|
| Convert between fractions, decimals and percentages. | Q1 ☐ | | |
| Use a multiplier to calculate percentage increase and decrease. | Q5 ☐ | | Q7 ☐ |
| Use the unitary method to solve percentage problems. | Q6 ☐ | | |
| Calculate compound interest. | Q8 ☐ | | |
| Simplify and use ratios involving decimals. | Q3 ☐ | | |
| Write and compare unit ratios. | Q4 ☐ | | |
| Divide a quantity into three parts in a given ratio. | Q2 ☐ | | |
| **My confidence** ☹◯ ☺◯ ☺◯ | | | |

**9**  Shapes and angles

| I can... | Unit 9: Unit test | | | | |
|---|---|---|---|---|---|
| Use properties of quadrilaterals. | Q1 ☐ | | Q3 ☐ | | |
| Solve problems using properties of angles in intersecting and parallel lines and polygons. | Q2 ☐ | | Q4 ☐ | | |
| Work out the interior and exterior angles of a polygon. | Q5 ☐ | | Q6 ☐ | | Q7 ☐ |
| **My confidence** ☹◯ ☺◯ ☺◯ | | | | | |

**10** Charts and diagrams

| I can... | Unit 10: Unit test |
|---|---|
| Calculate the mean from a frequency table. | Q2 ☐ |
| Interpret stem and leaf diagrams. | Q3 ☐ |
| Draw and interpret pie charts. | Q1 ☐ |
| Compare two sets of data using statistics or the shape of the graph. | Q4 ☐ |
| Interpret and draw scatter graphs. | Q5 ☐ |
| **My confidence** ☹○  😐○  ☺○ | |

**11** Straight-line graphs

| I can... | Unit 11: Unit test | | | |
|---|---|---|---|---|
| Plot straight-line graphs. | Q1 ☐ | | | |
| Find the gradient of a straight-line graph. | Q5 ☐ | | | |
| Find the equation of a straight-line graph. | Q6 ☐ | | | |
| Use $y = mx + c$. | Q2 ☐ | Q3 ☐ | Q4 ☐ | Q7 ☐ |
| **My confidence** ☹○  😐○  ☺○ | | | | |